# M A P

## INTERMEDIATE
## COMMUNICATION ARTS
## TEST PREPARATION

McDougal Littell
A HOUGHTON MIFFLIN COMPANY
Evanston, Illinois • Boston • Dallas

ISBN 0-618-24983-4

1 2 3 4 5 6 7 8 9 – DAM – 05 04 03 02

# Contents

# Note to the Teacher

Seventh-grade students in Missouri are required to take the *Missouri Assessment Program* (MAP) Intermediate Test in Communication Arts for grade 7. The MAP test in Intermediate Communication Arts assesses student attainment of the Show-Me Standards at the middle-school level. The test was developed to evaluate students' progress towards these academic standards, which define the knowledge, skills and competencies required of Missouri middle-school students. The MAP Intermediate Test in Communication Arts consists of constructed-response questions based upon a reading selection, and writing prompts that emphasize expository writing.

## About this Book

The *MAP Intermediate Communication Arts Test Preparation* book contains materials designed to help you prepare your students for the MAP Intermediate Test in Communication Arts. It provides MAP test practice that is related to specific reading selections taken from McDougal Littell's Grade 7 *Language of Literature* textbook. The answer key provided shows teachers examples of top-score responses to the constructed-response questions. Writing prompts are also included throughout the book to coincide with the *Language of Literature* writing workshops. A MAP scoring rubric for the writing prompts is included following the answer key. The *MAP Intermediate Communication Arts Test Preparation* book is designed using the same format as the MAP Intermediate Test, and will help create familiarity with the MAP throughout the school year and build student confidence as the test approaches.

NAME _____  DATE _____

## Seventh Grade

*(page 20)*

**1** Victor has decided to take a course in French. Identify <u>two</u> reasons why using details and/or examples from the story.

1. _____

_____

2. _____

_____

**2** Explain why Victor's friend Michael has started to scowl frequently. Use details and/or examples from the story to support your explanation.

_____

_____

_____

_____

_____

_____

NAME _____  DATE _____

## Seventh Grade *continued*

**3** Victor volunteers to speak French in class. Compare Teresa's reaction to Victor's performance with Victor's own reaction to his performance. Use details and/or examples from the story to support your explanation.

_____

_____

_____

_____

_____

**4** Why does Victor go outside during his lunch break? Use details and/or examples from the story to support your explanation.

_____

_____

_____

_____

_____

## *Thank You, M'am*

(page 29)

**1** Although the story doesn't say where it takes place, you can still tell a lot about its setting and the time of day when it takes place.

Use descriptions from the story to complete the chart below with examples that describe the story's setting or the time of day when it takes place. Then support your answers with evidence from the story. One has been completed.

### SETTING OF "THANK YOU, M'AM"

| Setting and Time of Day | Story Detail |
|---|---|
| **It is nighttime.** | **"Goodnight! Behave yourself, boy!"** |
| 1. | |
| 2. | |
| 3. | |

**2** Explain why Mrs. Jones takes Roger to her house. Use details and/or examples from the story to support your explanation.

_____

_____

_____

_____

_____

**3** Think about the two characters, Roger and Mrs. Jones, from the short story "Thank You, M'am." In the space below, construct a graphic organizer that shows how they are similar and how they are different. Use details and information from the story in your answer.

Your graphic organizer may be a chart, graph, diagram, drawing, cluster, web, mind map, or other organizer you feel is appropriate. Be sure to label your graphic organizer appropriately.

# If I Can Stop One Heart from Breaking (page 33)

**1** What are the goals of the poem's narrator? Use details and/or examples from the poem to support your explanation.

_____

_____

_____

_____

_____

_____

**2** Think about the similarities between Mrs. Jones in "Thank You, M'am" and the narrator of the poem "If I Can Stop One Heart from Breaking." How do these two passages illustrate similarities between these two characters? Use details and/or examples from the passages to support your explanation.

_____

_____

_____

_____

_____

_____

UNIT 1

NAME _____ DATE _____

# Names/Nombres

(page 37)

**1** The narrator of this essay says that her teacher and classmates called her different names than the one her parents called her. List <u>three</u> names that the narrator was called when she was outside her home.

1. _____

2. _____

3. _____

**2** Explain what the narrator means when she says that introducing her family members to her friends "was a further trial to me." Use details and/or examples from the essay to support your explanation.

_____

_____

_____

_____

_____

NAME _____ DATE _____

## Names/Nombres continued

**3** Why did Julia's friends want to hear her say her name, and what was unusual about this name? Use details and/or examples from the essay to support your explanation.

_____

_____

_____

_____

_____

**4** Explain the importance of the most significant graduation gift that the narrator received. Use details and/or examples from the essay to support your explanation.

_____

_____

_____

_____

_____

## Zebra

**1** Explain why Mr. Wilson asked Zebra to write the name "Leon" on the drawing that he had made for Mr. Wilson. Use details and/or examples from the story to support your explanation.

_____

_____

_____

_____

_____

**2** The narrator never fully explains the accident that caused Zebra's injuries. The narrator refers to "a huge rushing shadow." What do you think happened to Zebra? Use details and/or examples from the story to support your explanation.

_____

_____

_____

_____

_____

**3** In the space below, make a drawing of Mr. Wilson from the short story "Zebra." Your drawing should illustrate a specific scene from the story. While your drawing should be based on a scene from the story, feel free to also use your imagination to add extra details. After you complete your drawing, add a caption that explains the scene. Use details and/or examples from the story in your caption.

NAME _____ DATE _____

# *The Rider*

(page 61)

**1** Describe what the narrator is feeling at the end of the poem. Use details and/or examples from the poem to support your explanation.

_____

_____

_____

_____

_____

**2** What is the narrator doing in the poem's second stanza (lines 7 through 10)? Use details and/or examples from the poem to support your explanation.

_____

_____

_____

_____

NAME _____ DATE _____

# Offerings at The Wall

*(page 65)*

**1** Explain why people bring objects and letters to the Vietnam Veterans Memorial. Use details and/or examples from the article to support your explanation.

_____

_____

_____

_____

_____

_____

**2** What do you think is the most unusual gift or offering that is mentioned in the article? Explain why you think this is so unusual.

_____

_____

_____

_____

**3** In the space below, draw a diagram of the Vietnam Veterans Memorial. In this diagram, include The Wall as well as some offerings. Use your imagination for the offerings. Make sure that your diagram is labeled properly. Include details and/or examples from the article in your diagram.

NAME _____ DATE _____

## A Crush

(page 68)

**1** Ernie has a great interest in growing flowers. Explain how he first developed this interest in growing flowers. Use details and/or examples from the story to support your explanation.

_____

_____

_____

_____

_____

_____

**2** Ernie grows many types of flowers, and Jack grows many types of plants. In the chart below, name two other flowers and two other plants that these characters grow in their gardens. One item has already been added to each column of the chart. Use details and/or examples from the story to complete the chart.

FLOWERS AND PLANTS IN "A CRUSH"

Ernie's Flowers                              Jack's Plants

| Zinnias | Red radishes |
|---|---|
| 1. | 1. |
| 2. | 2. |

**3** Explain how Dolores is different from most of the female customers who come into the hardware store to buy "a package of light bulbs or some batteries." Use details and/or examples from the story to support your explanation.

_____

_____

_____

_____

**4** Why does Dolores not know the identity of the person who is bringing her flowers? Use details and/or examples from the story to support your explanation.

_____

_____

_____

_____

**5** Explain why, at the end of the story, Jack installs a long light in the basement of the group home. Use details and/or examples from the story to support your explanation.

_____

_____

_____

_____

_____

NAME _____   DATE _____

# WRITING

### Directions

Now you will write a paper in response to a writing prompt. First, read the prompt in the box below.

Then use the separate paper your teacher has given you for your prewriting activity (such as brainstorming, listing, freewriting, clustering, mapping, or drawing).

After you finish your prewriting activity, write your first draft on the separate paper your teacher has given you. Look back at your prewriting activity for ideas.

## Writing Prompt

In the short story "A Crush," Jack spends a lot of time helping a man named Ernie. Write a paper about a job that involves helping other people. Explain why this job is important, and how you could learn more about it.

# FINAL COPY

**Directions**

Now you have time to revise your draft. Reread your draft and think about the Writer's Checklist below. Check every box that makes a true statement about your draft.

## Writer's Checklist

☐ My paper has a beginning, middle, and end.

☐ My paper uses paragraphing appropriately.

☐ My paper flows smoothly from one idea to another.

☐ My paper stays on the topic.

☐ My paper includes details and examples.

☐ My paper uses precise and vivid language.

☐ My paper includes a variety of sentence structures.

☐ My paper includes correct grammar usage, punctuation, capitalization, and spelling.

For every box you did not check, make the necessary revisions on your draft before you write your final copy.

NAME _____ DATE _____

# *Eleanor Roosevelt*

*(page 87)*

**1** Eleanor Roosevelt had a difficult childhood. In the chart below, list three things that made her childhood particularly hard. Use details and/or examples from the biography to fill in the chart.

### Difficult Things About Eleanor Roosevelt's Childhood

| |
|---|
| 1. |
| 2. |
| 3. |

**2** Theodore Roosevelt, Eleanor Roosevelt, and Franklin Delano Roosevelt were all related, and they were all born with the same last name. Explain how Eleanor was related to Theodore, and to Franklin, who would become her husband. Use details from the biography to support your explanation.

_____

_____

_____

_____

_____

# *Eleanor Roosevelt* continued

**3** Eleanor Roosevelt was a very public figure during the time that Franklin Delano Roosevelt was president of the United States. Explain why the author calls Eleanor "the president's conscience." Use details and/or examples from the biography to support your explanation.

_____

_____

_____

_____

_____

_____

**4** Eleanor Roosevelt grew up to be a famous leader. When she was a child, it would have been difficult to predict that she would become famous around the world. Explain how Eleanor Roosevelt the adult was very different from Eleanor Roosevelt the child. Use details and/or examples from the biography to support your explanation.

_____

_____

_____

_____

_____

_____

# The Autobiography of Eleanor Roosevelt  (page 97)

**1** Although the subject is the same, a biography is quite different from an autobiography. Explain one important difference between William Jay Jacobs' biography "Eleanor Roosevelt" and the passage from *The Autobiography of Eleanor Roosevelt*. Use details and/or examples from the passages to support your explanation.

_____

_____

_____

_____

_____

_____

NAME _____  DATE _____

# No Ordinary Time

(page 97)

**1** The description of Eleanor Roosevelt in William Jay Jacobs' biography is similar to the excerpt from Doris Kearns Goodwin's book *No Ordinary Time*. What personality trait do both Jacobs and Goodwin describe? Use details and/or examples from the passages to support your explanation.

_____

_____

_____

_____

_____

_____

## Homeless

*(page 101)*

**1**  The narrator uses specific details to describe the inside of a home. Identify <u>two</u> of these descriptive details from the essay.

1. _____

_____

2. _____

_____

**2**  Inside a bus station, the narrator talks to a woman who carries with her a photograph of a yellow house. Explain why this photograph has special meaning for the woman. Use details and/or examples from the essay to support your explanation.

_____

_____

_____

_____

_____

_____

## Homeless continued

**3** Explain the main idea of the personal essay "Homeless." Use details and/or examples from the essay to support your explanation.

_____

_____

_____

_____

_____

_____

**4** In her personal essay "Homeless," Anna Quindlen describes things that make her own home feel comfortable and familiar. There are certain unique things that make a home feel like a home. In the chart below, fill in three specific things that make your home special. You can fill in one item for each area/room, or you could fill in three items from one area/room, but make sure to list three things.

| Room or Area of Your Home | Item |
|---|---|
| Bedroom or Sleeping Area | |
| Kitchen Area | |
| Living Room or Other Area | |

NAME _____ DATE _____

## Bums in the Attic *from* **The House on Mango Street**  (page 105)

**1** The narrator says that she no longer enjoys the Sunday trips with her family. Explain why she no longer enjoys these trips. Use details and/or examples from the passage to support your explanation.

_____

_____

_____

_____

_____

**2** Explain why the narrator says that in the future, she will allow "bums" to sleep in her attic. Use details and/or examples from the passage to support your explanation.

_____

_____

_____

_____

_____

UNIT 1

**3** What is a personality trait or a point of view that is shared by both the narrator of "Homeless" and the narrator of "Bums in the Attic"? Use details and/or examples from the passages to support your explanation.

_____

_____

_____

_____

_____

_____

## The War of the Wall

*(page 109)*

**1** Although the story doesn't say where it takes place, you can still tell a lot about its setting.

Use descriptions from the story to complete the chart below with examples that describe the story's setting, including the location and the time period. Then support your answers with evidence from the story. One has been completed.

### SETTING OF "THE WAR OF THE WALL"

| Location and Time Period | Story Detail |
|---|---|
| **A city not far from a rural area** | **The family takes a car trip to visit Grandma, who lives on a farm.** |
| 1. | |
| 2. | |
| 3. | |

**2** Explain who Jimmy Lyons was and why he is an important character in the story. Use details and/or examples from the story to support your explanation.

_____

_____

_____

_____

_____

## The War of the Wall continued

**3** Explain why, at first, Lou and the narrator dislike the painter. Use details and/or examples from the story to support your explanation.

_____

_____

_____

_____

_____

**4** The mural in this short story depicts famous African Americans, such as Dr. Martin Luther King, Jr., Malcolm X, Harriet Tubman, and Fannie Lou Hamer. The mural also depicts people who are not famous. What is unusual about these other people depicted in the mural? Use details and/or examples from the story to support your explanation.

_____

_____

_____

_____

_____

_____

NAME _____ DATE _____

# Song of Myself

(page 117)

**1** Describe what the narrator of this poem thinks about himself or herself. Use details and/or examples from the poem to support your explanation.

_____

_____

_____

_____

_____

_____

NAME _____ DATE _____

# Rikki-tikki-tavi

*(page 121)*

**1** In the short story "Rikki-tikki-tavi," the snake Nag hides around a water jar. Explain why Nag decided to hide there. Use details and/or examples from the story to support your explanation.

_____

_____

_____

_____

_____

_____

**2** On his first night in the house, Rikki-tikki sleeps in Teddy's room. What is Teddy's father's reaction to this, and what is Teddy's mother's reaction? Explain why they have different opinions about this situation. Use details and/or examples from the story to support your explanation.

_____

_____

_____

_____

_____

NAME _____  DATE _____

# Rikki-tikki-tavi continued

**3** When a writer gives human qualities to an animal, object, or idea, the technique is called personification. The animal characters in "Rikki-tikki-tavi" all act like people. Use descriptions from the story to complete the chart below with examples of personification. One has been completed.

### USE OF PERSONIFICATION IN "RIKKI-TIKKI-TAVI"

Animal Character        Human Quality or Characteristic

| Nagaina | sneaky |
|---|---|
| 1. Nag | |
| 2. Rikki-tikki | |
| 3. Chuchundra | |

**4** Explain Rikki-tikki's opinion of the bird Darzee. Use details and/or examples from the story to support your explanation.

_____

_____

_____

_____

_____

_____

NAME _____ DATE _____

# Primal Compassion

(page 138)

**1** In the concluding paragraph of this magazine article, Bob Allison asks a question: "If this animal that's supposed to be below us can be this way, why can't we?" In your own words, summarize the main idea of this question. Use details and/or examples from the article to support your explanation.

_____

_____

_____

_____

_____

_____

**2** The magazine article states that Eric was angry at his father, Bob, because he had photographed the event at the zoo. Explain why Eric was angry about this. Use details and/or examples from the article to support your explanation.

_____

_____

_____

_____

_____

_____

## Primal Compassion continued

**3** Think about the way that the animal characters treat the human characters in both "Rikki-tikki-tavi" and "Primal Compassion." In the space below, construct a graphic organizer that shows how Rikki-tikki the mongoose and Binti Jua the gorilla are similar and how they are different. Use details and information from the passages in your answer.

Your graphic organizer may be a chart, graph, diagram, drawing, cluster, web, mind map, or other organizer you feel is appropriate. Be sure to label your graphic organizer appropriately.

UNIT 1

## Dirk the Protector

**(page 143)**

**1** Explain how the narrator met Dirk, and how the two of them became companions. Use details and/or examples from the story to support your explanation.

_____

_____

_____

_____

_____

_____

**2** The narrator says that one boy was "absurdly" named "Happy" Santum. Explain why the narrator thinks that this is an absurd, or ridiculous, name. Use details and/or examples from the story to support your explanation.

_____

_____

_____

_____

_____

_____

NAME _____  DATE _____

## Dirk the Protector *continued*

**3** The narrator of "Dirk the Protector" mentions a few of the jobs that he had. Identify <u>two</u> of them using details and/or examples from the story.

1. _____

_____

2. _____

_____

**4** Toward the end of the story, the narrator says, "Dirk came to a wonderful end." Explain what the narrator means. Use details and/or examples from the story to support your explanation.

_____

_____

_____

_____

_____

_____

**5** In an earlier part of the story, the narrator has a rare treat in the form of a hamburger. Explain how the narrator got this hamburger. Use details and/or examples from the story to support your explanation.

_____

_____

_____

_____

_____

NAME _____  DATE _____

# O. Henry

*(page 150)*

**1** At the time of his death, the writer known as O. Henry refused to reveal his real birth name. Why do you think he did this? Use details and/or examples from the essay to support your answer.

_____

_____

_____

_____

_____

**2** Explain what the deaths of O. Henry's mother, grandmother, and first wife indicate about medicine in his day. Use details and/or examples from the story to support your explanation.

_____

_____

_____

_____

_____

NAME _____ DATE _____

## *After Twenty Years*

(page 154)

**1** The stories of O. Henry often include a surprise ending. Explain the great surprise, or twist, in this short story. Use details and/or examples from the story to support your answer.

_____

_____

_____

_____

_____

**2** The author describes the jewelry and fashion accessories that Bob has. What do you think these details suggest about Bob? Use details and/or examples from the story to support your answer.

_____

_____

_____

_____

_____

UNIT 1

NAME _____ DATE _____

## After Twenty Years continued

**3** Explain how Bob and Jimmy have changed over the course of the last twenty years. Use details and/or examples from the story to support your explanation.

_____

_____

_____

_____

_____

**4** Patrolman Wells recognized Bob as a criminal, but he did not arrest him. Explain why the patrolman did not make the arrest. Use details and/or examples from the story to support your explanation.

_____

_____

_____

_____

_____

NAME _____   DATE _____

# A Retrieved Reformation

*(page 163)*

**1** At the end of "A Retrieved Reformation," Ben Price refers to Jimmy Valentine as "Mr. Spencer." Explain why Ben Price uses this name. Use details and/or examples from the story to support your explanation.

_____

_____

_____

_____

_____

_____

**2** What does Jimmy Valentine's letter to his "Old Pal" indicate about Jimmy's personality? Use details and/or examples from the story to support your answer.

_____

_____

_____

_____

_____

_____

Copyright © McDougal Littell Inc.
All rights reserved.

NAME _____ DATE _____

# A Retrieved Reformation *continued*

**3** The author does not directly state that Jimmy Valentine cracked the safes in Richmond, Logansport, and Jefferson City. Explain why you think Jimmy did or did not commit those burglaries. Use details and/or examples from the story to support your explanation.

_____

_____

_____

_____

_____

**4** Explain why Jimmy Valentine registered at the Planters' Hotel under the name "Ralph D. Spencer." Use details and/or examples from the story to support your answer.

_____

_____

_____

_____

_____

# From Short Story to Big Screen *(page 173)*

**1** The play "Alias Jimmy Valentine" started a trend of plays (and later, films) that focused upon gangsters and detectives. Why do you think that this type of play/film became and remains so popular? Use details and/or examples from the passages to support your answer.

_____

_____

_____

_____

_____

NAME _____ DATE _____

## *Writing*

### Directions

Now you will write a paper in response to a writing prompt. First, read the prompt in the box below.

Then use the separate paper your teacher has given you for your prewriting activity (such as brainstorming, listing, freewriting, clustering, mapping, or drawing).

After you finish your prewriting activity, write your first draft on the separate paper your teacher has given you. Look back at your prewriting activity for ideas.

## Writing Prompt

The short story "A Retrieved Reformation" has a surprising twist at the end. Write about something that you saw or experienced that had a surprising twist. Explain how this event was unusual or why it turned out differently from the way most people expected it to end.

NAME _____  DATE _____

# Writing

### Directions

Now you have time to revise your draft. Reread your draft and think about the Writer's Checklist below. Check every box that makes a true statement about your draft.

## Writer's Checklist

☐ My paper has a beginning, middle, and end.

☐ My paper uses paragraphing appropriately.

☐ My paper flows smoothly from one idea to another.

☐ My paper stays on the topic.

☐ My paper includes details and examples.

☐ My paper uses precise and vivid language.

☐ My paper includes a variety of sentence structures.

☐ My paper includes correct grammar usage, punctuation, capitalization, and spelling.

For every box you did not check, make the necessary revisions on your draft before you write your final copy.

NAME _____ DATE _____

# The Pasture

*(page 196)*

**1** The narrator of "The Pasture" describes scenes and events that he enjoys observing. Identify <u>two</u> of them using details and/or examples from the poem.

1. _____

_____

2. _____

_____

**2** The mood of a passage is the feeling that the writer creates for the reader. Notice that lines 4 and 8 of the poem are exactly the same. Explain what effect these two lines have on the mood of this poem. Use details and/or examples from the poem to support your explanation.

_____

_____

_____

_____

**1** Although the poem doesn't say where it takes place, you can still tell a lot about its setting. Identify <u>two</u> details that show that this poem is set in the countryside, and not in a city.

1. _____

   _____

2. _____

   _____

**2** Think about the similarities between the narrator of "The Pasture" and the narrator of "A Time to Talk." How do these two poems illustrate similarities between these two narrators? Use details and/or examples from the poems to support your explanation.

_____

_____

_____

_____

UNIT 2

NAME _____ DATE _____

# The World Is Not a Pleasant Place to Be *(page 201)*

**1** Explain the meaning of the first stanza (lines 1–3) and the fourth stanza (lines 11–13) of the poem. Use details and/or examples from the poem to support your explanation.

_____

_____

_____

_____

**2** When a writer gives human qualities to an animal, object, or idea, the technique is called personification. The aspects of nature in "The World Is Not a Pleasant Place to Be" act like people. Use descriptions from the poem to complete the chart below with examples of personification. One has been completed.

USE OF PERSONIFICATION IN
"THE WORLD IS NOT A PLEASANT PLACE TO BE"

| Aspect of Nature | Human Quality or Activity |
|---|---|
| **A river** | **can decide to stop flowing** |
| 1. | |
| 2. | |

**1** What are the goals of the narrator of "To You"? Use details and/or examples from the poem to support your explanation.

_____

_____

_____

_____

**2** What type of people would the narrator of "To You" like to meet? Use details and/or examples from the poem to support your explanation.

_____

_____

_____

_____

UNIT 2

NAME _____ DATE _____

# What Do Fish Have to Do with Anything? *(page 206)*

**1** When Willie's mother is preparing a snack for him, why does she carefully measure the slice of cake? Use details and/or examples from the story to support your explanation.

_____

_____

_____

_____

**2** Explain why Willie's mother asks him to tell her four different phone numbers before she leaves for work at night. Use details and/or examples from the story to support your explanation.

_____

_____

_____

_____

**3** At the end of the story, the boy yells to his mother, "My name's not Willie. It's William." Explain why Willie now wants to be called William. Use details and/or examples from the story to support your explanation.

_____

_____

_____

_____

**4** *Dialogue* is a term that refers to conversation between characters in a passage. The short story "What Do Fish Have to Do with Anything?" includes a great deal of dialogue. Willie's dialogue often includes questions. Why do you think that Willie asks so many questions? Use details and/or examples from the story to support your answer.

_____

_____

_____

_____

UNIT 2

NAME _____ DATE _____

### from *Immigrant Kids*

*(page 223)*

**1** In the early 1900s, how did most immigrants arrive in the United States? Use details and/or examples from the passage to support your answer.

_____

_____

_____

_____

**2** At Ellis Island, why were immigrants closely examined for symptoms of trachoma? Use details and/or examples from the passage to support your answer.

_____

_____

_____

_____

NAME _____ DATE _____

## from *Immigrant Kids* continued

**3** Registration clerks at Ellis Island asked immigrants a series of questions, including this one: "Have you ever been in prison?" Explain why immigrants were asked this question. Use details from the passage to support your answer.

_____

_____

_____

_____

NAME _____ DATE _____

# *WRITING*

### Directions

Now you will write a paper in response to a writing prompt. First, read the prompt in the box below.

Then use the separate paper your teacher has given you for your prewriting activity (such as brainstorming, listing, freewriting, clustering, mapping, or drawing).

After you finish your prewriting activity, write your first draft on the separate paper your teacher has given you. Look back at your prewriting activity for ideas.

## Writing Prompt

> The passage from *Immigrant Kids* discusses the important journey that many Europeans made so that they could settle in the United States. Write a paper about an important journey that you have taken or you would like to take. Explain the importance of this journey to your life.

NAME _____  DATE _____

# FINAL COPY

### Directions

Now you have time to revise your draft. Reread your draft and think about the Writer's Checklist below. Check every box that makes a true statement about your draft.

## Writer's Checklist

☐ My paper has a beginning, middle, and end.

☐ My paper uses paragraphing appropriately.

☐ My paper flows smoothly from one idea to another.

☐ My paper stays on the topic.

☐ My paper includes details and examples.

☐ My paper uses precise and vivid language.

☐ My paper includes a variety of sentence structures.

☐ My paper includes correct grammar usage, punctuation, capitalization, and spelling.

For every box you did not check, make the necessary revisions on your draft before you write your final copy.

NAME _____  DATE _____

# A Christmas Carol

*(page 250)*

**1** Explain the stage direction that indicates Sparsit will extend his hand toward Scrooge for a coin. Why does Sparsit make this gesture? Use details and/or examples from the play to support your answer.

_____

_____

_____

_____

**2** The First Spirit allows Scrooge to see himself as a boy. Describe the types of books that Child Scrooge enjoyed reading. Use details and/or examples from the play to support your answer.

_____

_____

_____

_____

NAME _____ DATE _____

# A Christmas Carol continued

**3** According to the stage directions, the Second Spirit imitates Scrooge, repeating things that he had said earlier, such as this: "If he be like to die, he had better do it and decrease the surplus population." Explain why the Second Spirit repeats Scrooge's words back to him. Use details and/or examples from the play to support your explanation.

_____

_____

_____

_____

**4** In the beginning of the play's final scene, Scrooge says, "Spirit, hear me. I am not the man I was. I will not be that man that I have been for so many years." Explain the meaning of this speech and its overall importance to the play. Use details and/or examples from the play to support your explanation.

_____

_____

_____

_____

**5** Explain the theme of "A Christmas Carol." Use details and/or examples from the play to support your answer.

_____

_____

_____

_____

NAME _____  DATE _____

## *The Scholarship Jacket*    *(page 278)*

**1** Mr. Boone somehow thinks that Joann, not Martha, should be the winner of the scholarship jacket. Explain why Martha deserves to win the jacket. Use details and/or examples from the story to support your explanation.

_____

_____

_____

_____

**2** Martha is currently taking several classes at school. List <u>three</u> subjects that she is studying, using details and/or examples from the story.

1. _____

2. _____

3. _____

NAME _____  DATE _____

## The Scholarship Jacket continued

**3** Think about the ways that this short story shows many aspects of Martha's personality. In the space below, construct a graphic organizer that shows what type of person Martha is. Use details and information from the story in your answer.

Your graphic organizer may be a chart, graph, diagram, drawing, cluster, web, mind map, or other organizer you feel is appropriate. Be sure to label your graphic organizer appropriately.

NAME _____  DATE _____

## The Noble Experiment *from* **I Never Had it Made**  *(page 287)*

**1** Branch Rickey told Jackie Robinson that he would face many difficulties as the first African-American baseball player in the major leagues. Identify two of these difficulties using details and/or examples from the passage.

1. _____

_____

2. _____

_____

**2** Who was Wendell Smith, and what role did he play in Jackie Robinson's career? Use details and/or examples from the passage to support your answer.

_____

_____

_____

_____

**MAP Test Practice**

**3** Explain why Branch Rickey called Jackie Robinson "all kinds of foul racial names" while the two men were meeting in Mr. Rickey's office. Use details and/or examples from the passage to support your answer.

_____

_____

_____

_____

**4** Why did Jackie Robinson accept Branch Rickey's offer to play in the major leagues? Use details and/or examples from the passage to support your answer.

_____

_____

_____

_____

**1** In line 29 of "Casey at the Bat," the poet refers to the baseball as a "leather-covered sphere," and in line 39, it is called a "spheroid." Explain why the poet chose to use these words instead of simply calling it "the ball."

_____

_____

_____

_____

**2** Is Casey considered to be a good baseball player? Use details and/or examples from the poem to support your answer.

_____

_____

_____

_____

NAME _____ DATE _____

## Casey at the Bat *continued*

**3** Irony occurs in a literary work when there is a difference between what a reader expects to happen and what actually happens. Explain the use of irony in the poem "Casey at the Bat." Use details and/or examples from the poem to support your explanation.

_____

_____

_____

_____

**4** In the space below, make a diagram that illustrates the poem "Casey at the Bat." Your diagram should include Casey and the cheering crowd. Use your imagination to add extra details. Be sure to label your diagram appropriately.

NAME _____ DATE _____

# Fable: Ant and Grasshopper

*(page 312)*

**1** Explain why Ant refuses to share her grain with Grasshopper. Use details and/or examples from the fable to support your explanation.

_____

_____

_____

_____

**2** This fable is followed by the moral, which is a statement that explains the lesson of the story: "In good times prepare for when the bad times come." How does the moral of this fable relate to an experience that you may have had? Use details and/or examples from the fable to support your explanation.

_____

_____

_____

_____

# Poetry: The Ant and the Grasshopper   (page 312)

**1** A simile is a comparison that uses the signal word *like* or *as*. Identify <u>two</u> examples in this poem in which a simile is used to compare two things.

1. _____

_____

2. _____

_____

**2** Explain the moral, or the lesson, of the poem "The Ant and the Grasshopper." Use details and/or examples from the poem to support your explanation.

_____

_____

_____

_____

**3** Think about what happens in the fable "Ant and Grasshopper" and the poem "The Ant and the Grasshopper." Both of these passages tell the same story, but in a slightly different way. In the space below, construct a graphic organizer that shows how the two passages are similar and how they are different. Use details and information from the passages in your answer.

Your graphic organizer may be a chart, graph, diagram, drawing, cluster, web, mind map, or other organizer you feel is appropriate. Be sure to label your graphic organizer appropriately.

NAME _____ DATE _____

## The Richer, the Poorer

*(page 316)*

**1** Explain why Lottie never married. Use details and/or examples from the story to support your answer.

_____

_____

_____

_____

**2** There are many differences between Bess and Lottie. In the chart below, name two more differences between them. One item has already been added to each column of the chart. Use details and/or examples from the story to complete the chart.

DIFFERENCES BETWEEN BESS AND LOTTIE IN "THE RICHER, THE POORER"

|  Bess | Lottie |
|---|---|
| **married Harry** | **remained single** |
| 1. | 1. |
| 2. | 2. |

## The Richer, the Poorer

*(page 316)*

**3** Explain the moral, or the lesson, of the fable "The Richer, the Poorer." Use details and/or examples from the story to support your explanation.

_____

_____

_____

_____

NAME _____ DATE _____

# *WRITING*

### Directions

Now you will write a paper in response to a writing prompt. First, read the prompt in the box below.

Then use the separate paper your teacher has given you for your prewriting activity (such as brainstorming, listing, freewriting, clustering, mapping, or drawing).

After you finish your prewriting activity, write your first draft on the separate paper your teacher has given you. Look back at your prewriting activity for ideas.

## Writing Prompt

Imagine that you could trade places for one day with another person. With whom would you trade places, and why? Explain what you would do on your "trading places" day.

NAME _____  DATE _____

## *FINAL COPY*

### Directions

Now you have time to revise your draft. Reread your draft and think about the Writer's Checklist below. Check every box that makes a true statement about your draft.

## Writer's Checklist

☐ My paper has a beginning, middle, and end.

☐ My paper uses paragraphing appropriately.

☐ My paper flows smoothly from one idea to another.

☐ My paper stays on the topic.

☐ My paper includes details and examples.

☐ My paper uses precise and vivid language.

☐ My paper includes a variety of sentence structures.

☐ My paper includes correct grammar usage, punctuation, capitalization, and spelling.

For every box you did not check, make the necessary revisions on your draft before you write your final copy.

NAME _____ DATE _____

# One Ordinary Day, with Peanuts

*(page 348)*

**1** Explain why Mr. Johnson filled his pockets with peanuts. Use details and/or examples from the story to support your explanation.

_____

_____

_____

_____

**2** After Mr. Johnson met Mildred Kent, he carefully selected Arthur Adams out of a crowd. Explain why Mr. Johnson selected him so carefully. Use details and/or examples from the story to support your explanation.

_____

_____

_____

**3** Mr. Johnson interacts with many people during the course of his day.

Use descriptions from the story to complete the chart below with examples that describe the ways that Mr. Johnson interacts with different people. Then support your answers with actions from the story. One has been completed.

MR. JOHNSON'S ACTIONS IN "ONE ORDINARY DAY, WITH PEANUTS"

Name or Description of Character                Mr. Johnson's Action(s)

| **Arthur Adams** | **Mr. Johnson introduced Arthur Adams to Mildred Kent and gave the couple some money.** |
|---|---|
| 1. | |
| 2. | |
| 3. | |

**4** After Mr. Johnson returns home, he asks his wife, "Want to change over tomorrow?" Explain the meaning of this question and its importance to the entire story. Use details and/or examples from the story to support your explanation.

_____

_____

_____

_____

NAME _____ DATE _____

## Amigo Brothers

(page 361)

**1** This author of this story includes several standard Spanish words. He also includes some Spanish American expressions, which are a type of slang.

Use descriptions from the story and the footnotes to complete the chart below with Spanish (or Spanish American) words and their English translations. One has been completed.

LANGUAGE AND TRANSLATIONS IN "AMIGO BROTHERS"

Spanish (or Spanish American) Words          English Language Translation

| suavecito | Take it easy. |
|-----------|---------------|
| 1. | |
| 2. | |
| 3. | |

**2** Explain what Felix was thinking as he watched the film *The Champion*. Use details and/or examples from the story to support your explanation.

_____

_____

_____

_____

## Amigo Brothers *continued*

**3** There are many similarities between Antonio and Felix. Identify <u>three</u> similarities between these characters.

1. _____

2. _____

3. _____

**4** The author does not indicate who won the boxing match. This fight could not have ended in a draw, or tie, so there was one winner. Which boxer do you think was named the winner? Use details and/or examples from the story to support your answer.

_____

_____

_____

_____

NAME _____  DATE _____

# Ode to an Artichoke                                                    *(page 375)*

**1**  A metaphor is a literary device that compares two things that are basically unlike each other but that have something in common. What is the main metaphor of this poem? Use details and/or examples from the poem to support your answer.

_____

_____

_____

_____

**2**  The poem "Ode to an Artichoke" describes key events in the life of an artichoke. In the space below, construct a graphic organizer that shows the major events in the plant's life. Use details and information from the poem in your answer.

Your graphic organizer may be a chart, graph, diagram, drawing, cluster, web, mind map, or other organizer you feel is appropriate. Be sure to label your graphic organizer appropriately.

## *Ode to an Artichoke* *continued*

**3** When a writer gives human qualities to an animal, object, or idea, the technique is called personification. How does the poet use personification in his description of cabbage? Why is this an appropriate description of this leafy plant? Use details and/or examples from the poem to support your answer.

_____

_____

_____

_____

NAME _____ DATE _____

## from *An American Childhood*

(page 381)

**1** The passage describes a dramatic chase involving the narrator, Mikey Fahey, and the driver of a black automobile. In the space below, draw a diagram of the chase scene.

Your diagram should include all three characters, as well as the following: (1) Reynolds Street, (2) the black Buick automobile, (3) Edgerton Avenue, and (4) the hilltop backyard where the chase ends. Use your imagination, but pay close attention to the passage's descriptive details. Be sure to label your diagram appropriately.

**2** A writer's use of exaggeration or overstatement for emphasis is called hyperbole. Identify and explain <u>two</u> examples of hyperbole in this passage.

1. _____

   _____

2. _____

   _____

**3** Explain the difference between the author's idea of a typical snowball and what is known as "an iceball." Use details and/or examples from the passage to support your answer.

_____

_____

_____

_____

**4** Do you think that the driver's angry lecture prevented the narrator from throwing snowballs at cars again? Use details and/or examples from the passage to support your answer.

_____

_____

_____

_____

NAME _____ DATE _____

## The Bat

(page 391)

**1** In this poem, the poet compares the bat to another animal. How does the poet make this comparison, and why? Use details and/or examples from the poem to support your answer.

_____

_____

_____

_____

**2** Describe the pattern of rhyming words in this poem. Use details and/or examples from the poem to support your answer.

_____

_____

_____

NAME _____ DATE _____

# Mooses

*(page 391)*

**1** What is the narrator's opinion of the moose? Use details and/or examples from the poem to support your answer.

_____

_____

_____

_____

**2** When a writer gives human qualities to an animal, object, or idea, the technique is called personification. This technique is used in both "The Bat" and "Mooses." Use descriptions from the poems to complete the chart below with examples of personification. One has been completed.

### USE OF PERSONIFICATION IN "THE BAT" AND "MOOSES"

Animal                                    Human Behavior or Trait

| **Bat** | **has facial expressions like a human's** |
|---------|-------------------------------------------|
| 1. Bat  |                                           |
| 2. Moose |                                          |
| 3. Moose |                                          |

NAME _____ DATE _____

# WRITING

### Directions

Now you will write a paper in response to a writing prompt. First, read the prompt in the box below.

Then use the separate paper your teacher has given you for your prewriting activity (such as brainstorming, listing, freewriting, clustering, mapping, or drawing).

After you finish your prewriting activity, write your first draft on the separate paper your teacher has given you. Look back at your prewriting activity for ideas.

## Writing Prompt

"The Bat" and "Mooses" are both poems that compare animals to human beings. Write a paper about another type of animal that is similar to a human being. Explain this animal's human characteristics or behavior.

# *FINAL COPY*

### Directions

Now you have time to revise your draft. Reread your draft and think about the Writer's Checklist below. Check every box that makes a true statement about your draft.

## Writer's Checklist

☐ My paper has a beginning, middle, and end.

☐ My paper uses paragraphing appropriately.

☐ My paper flows smoothly from one idea to another.

☐ My paper stays on the topic.

☐ My paper includes details and examples.

☐ My paper uses precise and vivid language.

☐ My paper includes a variety of sentence structures.

☐ My paper includes correct grammar usage, punctuation, capitalization, and spelling.

For every box you did not check, make the necessary revisions on your draft before you write your final copy.

# The Monsters Are Due on Maple Street  *(page 415)*

**1** A play written for television is called a teleplay. Explain how the stage directions for this teleplay are different from the stage directions for a drama that is performed in a theater. Use details and/or examples from the play to support your explanation.

_____

_____

_____

_____

**2** Explain why Charlie kills Pete Van Horn. Use details and/or examples from the play to support your explanation.

_____

_____

_____

_____

UNIT 3

# The Monsters Are Due on Maple Street continued

**3** In this play, why do people react so strongly to the news that Les Goodman stares at the stars and that Steve Brand tinkers with a radio set in his basement? Use details and/or examples from the play to support your answer.

_____

_____

_____

_____

**4** What is the theme, or main message, of this play? Use details and/or examples from the play to support your answer.

_____

_____

_____

_____

**5** What caused the power failure on Maple Street? Use details and/or examples from the play to support your answer.

_____

_____

_____

_____

**1** Identify <u>three</u> subjects or types of information that Multivac can process.

1. _____

2. _____

3. _____

**2** Think about the similarities and differences between the play "The Monsters Are Due on Maple Street" and the short story "Key Item." In the space below, construct a graphic organizer that shows how they are similar and how they are different. Use details and information from the passages in your answer.

Your graphic organizer may be a chart, graph, diagram, drawing, cluster, web, mind map, or other organizer you feel is appropriate. Be sure to label your graphic organizer appropriately.

NAME _____ DATE _____

## Key Item *continued*

**3** Explain why Multivac suddenly started working again on the twelfth attempt. Use details and/or examples from the story to support your answer.

_____

_____

_____

_____

NAME _____ DATE _____

# The Serial Garden

(page 438)

**1** At the end of "The Serial Garden," the author describes a classified advertisement that is placed in *The Times* newspaper. Who placed this advertisement, and why? Use details and/or examples from the story to support your answer.

_____

_____

_____

_____

**2** Explain how the author uses humor to describe the taste of Brekkfast Brikks. Use details and/or examples from the story to support your explanation.

_____

_____

_____

_____

**3** What caused the hole in the grotto of the princess's garden? Use details and/or examples from the story to support your answer.

_____

_____

_____

_____

**4** The story describes many aspects of the princess's garden. In the space below, draw a diagram of the garden. Use your imagination, but pay close attention to the story's descriptive details. Be sure to label your diagram appropriately.

NAME _____ DATE _____

# Jabberwocky

(page 458)

**1** Explain the plot of "Jabberwocky." What happens in this poem? Use details and/or examples from the poem to support your answer.

_____

_____

_____

_____

**2** What is the most unusual feature of this poem? Use details and/or examples from the poem to support your answer.

_____

_____

_____

_____

UNIT 3

NAME _____  DATE _____

# Sarah Cynthia Sylvia Stout Would Not Take the Garbage Out

*(page 458)*

**1** What is the moral, or lesson, of this humorous poem? Use details and/or examples from the poem to support your answer.

_____

_____

_____

_____

**2** Alliteration is the repetition of consonant sounds at the beginnings of words and syllables. Complete the chart below with phrases that contain alliteration. One has been completed.

### SPECIFIC TYPES OF ALLITERATION IN THE POEM

Consonant Sound                                                    Phrase

| **Repetition of the "S" Sound** | **"Sarah Cynthia Sylvia Stout"** |
|---|---|
| 1. Repetition of the "P" Sound | |
| 2. Repetition of the "G" Sound | |
| 3. Repetition of the "B" Sound | |

NAME _____ DATE _____

# Sarah Cynthia Sylvia Stout Would Not Take the Garbage Out

*continued*

**3** Compare "Jabberwocky" to "Sarah Cynthia Sylvia Stout Would Not Take the Garbage Out." Explain how these two poems are similar. Use details and/or examples from the poems to support your explanation.

_____

_____

_____

_____

NAME _____ .DATE _____

## The Eternal Frontier

(page 463)

**1** The author states this fact: "In 1900 there were 144 miles of surfaced road in the United States." What is the author's purpose for mentioning this fact in his essay? Use details and/or examples from the essay to support your answer.

_____

_____

_____

_____

**2** Explain this author's opinion of outer space exploration. Use details and/or examples from the essay to support your answer.

_____

_____

_____

_____

**MAP Test Practice**

**3** Imagine that you and the author of this essay are both guests on a talk show. You have been chosen to debate the author. If you were representing the opposing point of view, what would you say to support your reasons for disagreeing with the author's essay? Use details and/or examples from the essay to support your answer.

_____

_____

_____

_____

NAME _____ DATE _____

# Dark They Were, and Golden-Eyed    *(page 478)*

**1** In a passage with first-person point of view, the narrator uses pronouns like *I* and *me*. If the events are related from a third-person limited point of view, the narrator tells us what one character thinks, feels, and observes. Which point of view is used in this short story? Use details and/or examples from the story to support your answer.

_____

_____

_____

_____

**2** At the end of this story, the reader understands something that the lieutenant and the captain from Earth do not. What will happen to these two characters? Use details and/or examples from the story to support your explanation.

_____

_____

_____

_____

NAME _____ DATE _____

# Dark They Were, and Golden-Eyed (page 478)

**3** Why does the captain want to use names like "Lincoln Mountains" and "Washington Canal" for the landscape on Mars? Use details and/or examples from the story to support your explanation.

_____

_____

_____

_____

**4** Think about the way that the Bitterings' life on Mars is different from their previous life on Earth. In the space below, construct a graphic organizer that shows how their lives changed. Use details and information from the story in your answer.

Your graphic organizer may be a chart, graph, diagram, drawing, cluster, web, mind map, or other organizer you feel is appropriate. Be sure to label your graphic organizer appropriately.

**5** Explain why Harry Bittering abandons his plan to build a rocket. Use details and/or examples from the story to support your explanation.

_____

_____

_____

_____

NAME _____ DATE _____

# The Golden Kite, the Silver Wind (page 492)

**1** What is the moral, or lesson, of this short story? Use details and/or examples from the story to support your answer.

_____

_____

_____

_____

**2** In this short story, each town keeps changing its walls in response to what the neighboring town has done.

Use details from the story to complete the chart below. List the various shapes that were built in response to the neighboring town's wall shape. One has been completed.

THE CHANGING WALL SHAPES IN "THE GOLDEN KITE, THE SILVER WIND"

The Shape of the First Town's Wall          The Shape of the Kwan-Si Town Wall

| Orange | Pig |
|---|---|
| 1. Club | |
| 2. Lake | |
| 3. Needle | |

**3** Who is the wisest character in the story, and why? Use details and/or examples from the story to support your answer.

_____

_____

_____

_____

# WRITING

## Directions

Now you will write a paper in response to a writing prompt. First, read the prompt in the box below.

Then use the separate paper your teacher has given you for your prewriting activity (such as brainstorming, listing, freewriting, clustering, mapping, or drawing).

After you finish your prewriting activity, write your first draft on the separate paper your teacher has given you. Look back at your prewriting activity for ideas.

## Writing Prompt

Many inventions in the twentieth century made life easier. Write a paper about a future machine that could be invented in the next 100 years. Explain what this invention would do and how it would help people.

**Directions**

Now you have time to revise your draft. Reread your draft and think about the Writer's Checklist below. Check every box that makes a true statement about your draft.

## Writer's Checklist

☐ My paper has a beginning, middle, and end.

☐ My paper uses paragraphing appropriately.

☐ My paper flows smoothly from one idea to another.

☐ My paper stays on the topic.

☐ My paper includes details and examples.

☐ My paper uses precise and vivid language.

☐ My paper includes a variety of sentence structures.

☐ My paper includes correct grammar usage, punctuation, capitalization, and spelling.

For every box you did not check, make the necessary revisions on your draft before you write your final copy.

**1**  Writers may use figurative language when they choose words and phrases that help readers picture ordinary things in new ways. Explain the literal meaning of this sentence: "The umbrella glowed like a scepter on the blue carpet while Mona, slumping over the keyboard, managed to eke out a fair rendition of a cat fight." Use details and/or examples from the story to support your explanation.

_____

_____

_____

_____

**2**  Explain why the narrator did not want to go back into Miss Crosman's house when it began to rain. Use details and/or examples from the story to support your explanation.

_____

_____

_____

_____

NAME _____ DATE _____

## The White Umbrella *continued*

**3** A person, place, object, or action that stands for something beyond itself is a symbol. What does the white umbrella symbolize, or represent, in this short story? Use details and/or examples from the story to support your explanation.

_____

_____

_____

_____

**4** Explain why the narrator's mother did not want to tell her daughters where she was working. Use details and/or examples from the story to support your explanation.

_____

_____

_____

_____

UNIT 4

NAME _____   DATE _____

## from *Boy: Tales of Childhood*   (page 533)

**1** Explain why the boy named Thwaites refused to eat licorice bootlaces. Use details and/or examples from the passage to support your explanation.

_____

_____

_____

_____

**2** A writer's use of exaggeration or overstatement for emphasis is called hyperbole. Name <u>two</u> examples of hyperbole in the passage, and explain what is being exaggerated.

1. _____

_____

2. _____

_____

**3** Explain why Mr. Coombes ordered the entire school to line up on the playground. Use details and/or examples from the passage to support your explanation.

_____

_____

_____

_____

## from *Boy: Tales of Childhood* continued

**4** Autobiographical writings give the reader a detailed understanding of the author's personality. In the space below, construct a graphic organizer that describes author Roald Dahl's personality when he was a boy. Use details and information from the passage in your answer.

Your graphic organizer may be a chart, graph, diagram, drawing, cluster, web, mind map, or other organizer you feel is appropriate. Be sure to label your graphic organizer appropriately.

**5** The author names several types of candy that were sold at Mrs. Pratchett's sweetshop. List <u>five</u> types of candy that were sold there.

1. _____

2. _____

3. _____

4. _____

5. _____

UNIT 4

# A Defenseless Creature

*(page 553)*

**1** A farce is a comedy that exaggerates plot, dialogue, and situation to amuse an audience. Describe <u>two</u> elements of this play that help make it a farce.

1. _____

_____

2. _____

_____

**2** Explain why the woman, Mrs. Schukin, has come to the bank to meet with Mr. Kistunov. Use details and/or examples from the play to support your explanation.

_____

_____

_____

_____

NAME _____ DATE _____

## A Defenseless Creature continued

**3** Imagine that you are responsible for the set design and stage props for a theatrical production of "A Defenseless Creature." Explain what items you would need to find (or build) for this play.

_____

_____

_____

_____

# The Highwayman

*(page 564)*

**1** In this poem, what happens to Bess, the landlord's daughter? Use details and/or examples from the poem to support your explanation.

_____

_____

_____

_____

**2** Although the poem doesn't say when it takes place, you can still tell a lot about its setting and the time period when it occurs. Describe the time period, or era, in which this poem is set. Use details and/or examples from the poem to support your explanation.

_____

_____

_____

_____

**3** Alliteration is the repetition of consonant sounds at the beginnings of words and syllables. Complete the chart below with phrases that contain alliteration. One has been completed.

### SPECIFIC TYPES OF ALLITERATION IN "THE HIGHWAYMAN"

Consonant Sound                                              Phrase

| Repetition of the "G" Sound | "a ghostly galleon" |
|---|---|
| 1. Repetition of the "C" Sound | |
| 2. Repetition of the "D" Sound | |
| 3. Repetition of the "L" Sound | |

# *WRITING*

**Directions**

Now you will write a paper in response to a writing prompt. First, read the prompt in the box below.

Then use the separate paper your teacher has given you for your prewriting activity (such as brainstorming, listing, freewriting, clustering, mapping, or drawing).

After you finish your prewriting activity, write your first draft on the separate paper your teacher has given you. Look back at your prewriting activity for ideas.

## Writing Prompt

In the poem "The Highwayman," Bess wears a red love-knot in her hair to symbolize her feelings of love. Write a paper about a symbolic item or article of clothing that you have worn. Explain what the item or clothing symbolized, and why that is important.

NAME _____  DATE _____

# WRITING

### Directions

Now you have time to revise your draft. Reread your draft and think about the Writer's Checklist below. Check every box that makes a true statement about your draft.

## Writer's Checklist

☐ My paper has a beginning, middle, and end.

☐ My paper uses paragraphing appropriately.

☐ My paper flows smoothly from one idea to another.

☐ My paper stays on the topic.

☐ My paper includes details and examples.

☐ My paper uses precise and vivid language.

☐ My paper includes a variety of sentence structures.

☐ My paper includes correct grammar usage, punctuation, capitalization, and spelling.

For every box you did not check, make the necessary revisions on your draft before you write your final copy.

# An Hour with Abuelo

*(page 591)*

**1** The author of this story includes several Spanish words and phrases.

Use descriptions from the story and the footnotes to complete the chart below with Spanish words (or phrases) and their English translations. One has been completed.

### LANGUAGE AND TRANSLATIONS IN "AN HOUR WITH ABUELO"

| Spanish Word or Phrase | English Language Translation |
|---|---|
| **abuelo** | **grandfather** |
| 1. | |
| 2. | |
| 3. | |

**2** The theme of a story is the meaning, moral, or main message the writer wishes to share with the reader. What is the theme of "An Hour with Abuelo"? Use details and/or examples from the story to support your answer.

_____

_____

_____

_____

**3** Explain why Arturo does not like the title of his grandfather's autobiographical book, *Así es la vida*. Use details and/or examples from the story to support your explanation.

_____

_____

_____

_____

**4** What will happen after the end of this story? If the story were to continue, explain what Arturo would do next. Use details and/or examples from the story to support your explanation.

_____

_____

_____

_____

UNIT 4

NAME _____ DATE _____

## Waiting

(page 601)

**1** How did Henrietta help Juliette (the narrator) during the children's summer play? Use details and/or examples from the story to support your explanation.

_____

_____

_____

_____

**2** Even though Juliette and Henrietta are twin sisters, they are very different from each other. Use descriptions from the story to complete the chart below with examples that describe the ways that the two girls are different. One has been completed.

### DIFFERENCES BETWEEN THE TWIN SISTERS IN "WAITING"

| Juliette | Henrietta |
|---|---|
| Dominant and bossy | Submissive and quiet |
| 1. | |
| 2. | |
| 3. | |

**3** Read this passage from the story: "But I put all I had into this first scene, because when Alphonse turns down all the eligible and less beautiful women of the land and retires to a corner of the stage to brood (with George Cruikshank standing nearby, munching grass), Genevieve arrives on the scene to a roll of drums (our wooden spoon on Mrs. Eisner's pickling kettle)." In this passage, explain the meaning of the comments enclosed in parentheses.

_____

_____

_____

_____

**4** Explain what "The Grove" was and why it was important in the story. Use details and/or examples from the story to support your explanation.

_____

_____

_____

_____

**5** Most works of fiction include four key elements: Exposition, Rising Action, Climax, and Falling Action (sometimes called Denouement).

The chart below lists these four key elements of the plot, and their functions. Use details from the story to fill in the last column of the chart, which lists examples of each key element. One has been completed.

THE PLOT OF "WAITING"

| PLOT ELEMENT | FUNCTION | EXAMPLE(S) |
|---|---|---|
| Exposition | introduces characters and setting | The main characters are Juliette and Henrietta. The setting is Canada in the early 1940s. |
| Rising Action | is where the main conflict unfolds | |
| Climax | is the turning point of the story | |
| Falling Action | follows the climax, and may provide a resolution to the main conflict | |

UNIT 4

**1** Explain why the author began selling copies of the *Saturday Evening Post*. Use details and/or examples from the passage to support your explanation.

_____

_____

_____

_____

**2** This passage is entertaining because of the author's use of humor. List two examples of humorous details in the passage, and explain why they are funny.

_____

_____

_____

_____

**3** By the end of this passage, the author has decided that he would like to be a writer one day. The author makes this comment: "Writers didn't have to have any gumption at all." In the context of this passage, explain what the author meant by this comment. Use details and/or examples from the passage to support your explanation.

_____

_____

_____

_____

**4** The passage describes the intersection of Belleville Avenue and Union Avenue, where the author tried to sell magazines. In the space below, draw a diagram of this scene.

Your diagram should include the author with his canvas bag, as well as the businesses in the area. Use your imagination, but pay close attention to the passage's descriptive details. Be sure to label your diagram appropriately.

UNIT 4

NAME _____  DATE _____

# WRITING

**Directions**

Now you will write a paper in response to a writing prompt. First, read the prompt in the box below.

Then use the separate paper your teacher has given you for your prewriting activity (such as brainstorming, listing, freewriting, clustering, mapping, or drawing).

After you finish your prewriting activity, write your first draft on the separate paper your teacher has given you. Look back at your prewriting activity for ideas.

## Writing Prompt

An autobiography is the story of a person's life told by that person. Write a paper about your early childhood, or about your current life. Explain where you grew up (or where you now live), and describe the people who have had a big impact on your life.

**Directions**

Now you have time to revise your draft. Reread your draft and think about the Writer's
Checklist below. Check every box that makes a true statement about your draft.

## Writer's Checklist

☐ My paper has a beginning, middle, and end.

☐ My paper uses paragraphing appropriately.

☐ My paper flows smoothly from one idea to another.

☐ My paper stays on the topic.

☐ My paper includes details and examples.

☐ My paper uses precise and vivid language.

☐ My paper includes a variety of sentence structures.

☐ My paper includes correct grammar usage, punctuation, capitalization, and spelling.

For every box you did not check, make the necessary revisions on your draft before you
write your final copy.

NAME _____   DATE _____

*from* **Exploring the Titanic**          *(page 658)*

**1** According to the passage and diagram, what items were stored in the forecastle area of the ship? Use details and/or examples from the passage to support your explanation.

_____

_____

_____

_____

**2** Explain the role that stokers played on the ship. Use details and/or examples from the passage to support your explanation.

_____

_____

_____

_____

NAME _____ DATE _____

## from *Exploring the Titanic* continued

**3** Explain why the author compares the *Titanic* to a layer cake. Use details and/or examples from the passage to support your explanation.

_____

_____

_____

_____

**4** The author names several ships besides the *Titanic*. List <u>three</u> of them.

1. _____

2. _____

3. _____

**5** Explain why the *Titanic* sank. Use details and/or examples from the passage to support your explanation.

_____

_____

_____

_____

**1** The narrator and his brother, Colin, have similarities and differences. In the space below, construct a graphic organizer that compares the two brothers. Use details and information from the story in your answer.

Your graphic organizer may be a chart, graph, diagram, drawing, cluster, web, mind map, or other organizer you feel is appropriate. Be sure to label your graphic organizer appropriately.

**2** Explain what the narrator's father meant when he said, "The seven sleepers are under cover." Use details and/or examples from the story to support your explanation.

_____

_____

_____

_____

NAME _____ DATE _____

## Last Cover continued

**3** Explain how Bandit was able to avoid the fox hunters for much of the day. Use details and/or examples from the story to support your explanation.

_____

_____

_____

_____

**4** Explain why, at first, the boys' father did not approve of keeping a fox as a pet. Use details and/or examples from the story to support your explanation.

_____

_____

_____

_____

**5** A person, place, object, or action that stands for something beyond itself is a symbol. What does Colin's framed drawing of the woods symbolize, or represent, in this short story? Use details and/or examples from the story to support your explanation.

_____

_____

_____

_____

UNIT 5

NAME _____ DATE _____

# WRITING

**Directions**

Now you will write a paper in response to a writing prompt. First, read the prompt in the box below.

Then use the separate paper your teacher has given you for your prewriting activity (such as brainstorming, listing, freewriting, clustering, mapping, or drawing).

After you finish your prewriting activity, write your first draft on the separate paper your teacher has given you. Look back at your prewriting activity for ideas.

## Writing Prompt

The short story "Last Cover" is about two brothers' love of a pet fox. Write a paper about your favorite pet or an animal that you admire. Explain what makes this animal so special.

NAME _____   DATE _____

# WRITING

### Directions

Now you have time to revise your draft. Reread your draft and think about the Writer's Checklist below. Check every box that makes a true statement about your draft.

## Writer's Checklist

☐ My paper has a beginning, middle, and end.

☐ My paper uses paragraphing appropriately.

☐ My paper flows smoothly from one idea to another.

☐ My paper stays on the topic.

☐ My paper includes details and examples.

☐ My paper uses precise and vivid language.

☐ My paper includes a variety of sentence structures.

☐ My paper includes correct grammar usage, punctuation, capitalization, and spelling.

For every box you did not check, make the necessary revisions on your draft before you write your final copy.

# A Crown of Wild Olive

(page 709)

**1** What was the Double Stade event? Use details and/or examples from the story to support your answer.

_____

_____

_____

_____

**2** Explain why it was difficult for Amyntas and Leon to become friends. Use details and/or examples from the story to support your explanation.

_____

_____

_____

_____

**3** If Leon had *not* cut his foot, how would the outcome of the race have been different? Use details and/or examples from the story to support your answer.

_____

_____

_____

_____

NAME _____ DATE _____

# A Crown of Wild Olive continued

**4** Explain why Leon did not buy anything from the tents and booths set up near the Games Festival. Use details and/or examples from the story to support your explanation.

_____

_____

_____

_____

**5** This story of two runners is set in ancient Greece. Over the centuries, many aspects of the Games have changed, but some aspects have remained basically the same. In the space below, construct a graphic organizer that compares the ancient Festival Games with today's modern Olympic Games. Use details and information from the story in your answer.

Your graphic organizer may be a chart, graph, diagram, drawing, cluster, web, mind map, or other organizer you feel is appropriate. Be sure to label your graphic organizer appropriately.

**1** A metaphor compares two things that seem dissimilar but have at least one thing in common. Writers make this comparison without using the words *like* or *as*. Name <u>two</u> metaphors from the passage, and for each one, explain what is being compared.

1. _____

_____

2. _____

_____

**2** At the end of the passage, Nelson Mandela writes, "I dare not linger, for my long walk is not yet ended." Explain the meaning of this sentence. Use details and/or examples from the passage to support your explanation.

_____

_____

_____

_____

**3** Explain why Nelson Mandela felt free when he was a boy, but not when he became an adult. Use details and/or examples from the passage to support your explanation.

_____

_____

_____

_____

NAME _____  DATE _____

## The Elephant

(page 740)

**1** Who is the narrator of this poem, and what emotion is the narrator feeling? Use details and/or examples from the poem to support your explanation.

_____

_____

_____

_____

**2** A literary work's tone describes the writer's attitude toward his or her subject. What is the tone of this poem? Use details and/or examples from the poem to support your explanation.

_____

_____

_____

_____

## The Turtle

*(page 740)*

**1** Explain what the turtle in this poem is doing. Use details and/or examples from the poem to support your explanation.

_____

_____

_____

_____

**2** The poet writes that the turtle is "only filled with an old blind wish." In the context of this poem, what is the meaning of this phrase? Use details and/or examples from the poem to support your explanation.

_____

_____

_____

_____

## The Turtle *continued*

**3** Compare the poem "The Elephant" to the poem "The Turtle." Explain how the poems are similar, and how they are different. Use details and/or examples from the poems to support your explanation.

_____

_____

_____

_____

## from *Anthony Burns:* *(page 750)*
## *The Defeat and Triumph of a Fugitive Slave*

**1** According to Judge Loring, there were three key facts that Charles Suttle's lawyers were required to prove. List all <u>three</u> of them.

1. _____

2. _____

3. _____

**2** Explain why the laws of the state of Virginia were so important to this trial, which took place in Boston, Massachusetts. Use details and/or examples from the passage to support your explanation.

_____

_____

_____

_____

**3** Describe Anthony Burns's mood and feelings during his trial. Use details and/or examples from the passage to support your answer.

_____

_____

_____

_____

## from **Anthony Burns:** *continued*
### *The Defeat and Triumph of a Fugitive Slave*

**4** Explain the purpose of the Boston Vigilance Committee. Use details and/or examples from the passage to support your explanation.

_____

_____

_____

_____

**5** Reverend Parker wrote a leaflet that was intended to inform abolitionists that an act of injustice was being done to Anthony Burns. In the space below, design your own, original leaflet that calls for Anthony Burns's freedom. Use details and information from the passage in your leaflet.

NAME _____ DATE _____

## The People Could Fly                    (page 767)

**1** Why do you think that slaves in the 1800s told this particular folk tale to one another? Use details and/or examples from the story to support your answer.

_____

_____

_____

_____

**2** Describe the ways in which the treatment of a slave was harsh and brutal. Use details and/or examples from the story to support your answer.

_____

_____

_____

_____

**3** The story includes a dramatic scene in which Toby helps Sarah to fly away from the Overseer and the Driver. In the space below, draw a diagram of this scene.

Your diagram should include Toby, Sarah, the Overseer, and the Driver. Be sure to label your diagram appropriately.

NAME _____  DATE _____

# WRITING

## Directions

Now you will write a paper in response to a writing prompt. First, read the prompt in the box below.

Then use the separate paper your teacher has given you for your prewriting activity (such as brainstorming, listing, freewriting, clustering, mapping, or drawing).

After you finish your prewriting activity, write your first draft on the separate paper your teacher has given you. Look back at your prewriting activity for ideas.

## Writing Prompt

Comic-book heroes and heroines often have super-human skills, such as the ability to leap over tall buildings. If you could have one super-human skill, what would it be? Write a paper about this skill and how you would use it to help other people.

NAME _____  DATE _____

# *WRITING*

### Directions

Now you have time to revise your draft. Reread your draft and think about the Writer's Checklist below. Check every box that makes a true statement about your draft.

## Writer's Checklist

☐ My paper has a beginning, middle, and end.

☐ My paper uses paragraphing appropriately.

☐ My paper flows smoothly from one idea to another.

☐ My paper stays on the topic.

☐ My paper includes details and examples.

☐ My paper uses precise and vivid language.

☐ My paper includes a variety of sentence structures.

☐ My paper includes correct grammar usage, punctuation, capitalization, and spelling.

For every box you did not check, make the necessary revisions on your draft before you write your final copy.

NAME _____ DATE _____

# *Prometheus* *(page 800)*

**1** Describe the relationship between Zeus and Prometheus. Use details and/or examples from the story to support your answer.

_____

_____

_____

_____

**2** Explain how fire changed the lives of humans in this myth. Use details and/or examples from the story to support your explanation.

_____

_____

_____

_____

## *Prometheus* continued

**3** After Zeus became angry, he said to himself, "Let them destroy themselves with their new skills." Explain the meaning of this sentence in this myth. Use details and/or examples from the story to support your explanation.

_____

_____

_____

_____

**4** Even before humans were given fire, Zeus thought that there was a key difference between a human and a beast. Explain this difference. Use details and/or examples from the story to support your explanation.

_____

_____

_____

_____

# Theseus and the Minotaur

*(page 804)*

**1** Explain how Theseus proved to King Aegeus that he was, indeed, his son. Use details and/or examples from the story to support your explanation.

_____

_____

_____

_____

**2** Explain the importance of the black sail and the white sail in this myth. Use details and/or examples from the story to support your explanation.

_____

_____

_____

_____

**3** Theseus may not have been able to defeat the Minotaur without the help of Ariadne. In the space below, construct a graphic organizer that describes the ways that Ariadne helped Theseus. Use details and information from the story in your answer.

Your graphic organizer may be a chart, graph, diagram, drawing, cluster, web, mind map, or other organizer you feel is appropriate. Be sure to label your graphic organizer appropriately.

**4** The god Dionysus took Ariadne's crown "and set it in the heavens, where each jewel became a star, and where it can still be seen." In the context of this myth, explain the meaning of Dionysus's actions. Use details and/or examples from the story to support your explanation.

_____

_____

_____

_____

NAME _____ DATE _____

# Waters of Gold

*(page 812)*

**1** This folk tale uses examples of figurative language, including the simile and the metaphor. A simile is a comparison that uses the signal word *like* or *as*. A metaphor is a direct comparison with no signal words. Complete the chart below by listing <u>two</u> more similes and <u>two</u> more metaphors from the story.

### FIGURATIVE LANGUAGE IN "WATERS OF GOLD"

| Simile (Using *like* or *as*) | Metaphor |
|---|---|
| **"His hair was as matted and muddy as a bird's nest."** | **"He was a ragbag of a man."** |
| 1. | 1. |
| 2. | 2. |

**2** Explain why the villagers ignored the beggar at first but then rushed to help him when he returned. Use details and/or examples from the story to support your explanation.

_____

_____

_____

_____

**3** Explain why the beggar tells the rich neighbor, "Dirt's dirt, and garbage is garbage."
Use details and/or examples from the story to support your explanation.

_____

_____

_____

_____

**4** A moral is a lesson that a story teaches. What is the moral of "Waters of Gold"? Use
details and/or examples from the story to support your answer.

_____

_____

_____

_____

NAME _____ DATE _____

# Ashputtle

*(page 818)*

**1** Ashputtle's cruel stepmother gives several reasons why Ashputtle is not allowed to attend the wedding celebration. List <u>three</u> of those reasons.

1. _____

2. _____

3. _____

**2** Explain why the king's son had the staircase covered with sticky pitch. Use details and/or examples from the story to support your explanation.

_____

_____

_____

_____

NAME _____  DATE _____

## Ashputtle continued

**3** Repetition is a key feature of oral literature. Name <u>two</u> examples of repetition in this folk tale, and explain what effect the repeating of these elements has on the reader or listener. Use details and/or examples from the story to support your explanation.

1. _____

_____

2. _____

_____

**4** Ashputtle's hazel tree was very special, and three times in the story she says, "Shake your branches, little tree/ Throw gold and silver down on me." In the space below, construct a graphic organizer that describes the importance of this tree in the story. Use details and information from the story in your answer.

Your graphic organizer may be a chart, graph, diagram, drawing, cluster, web, mind map, or other organizer you feel is appropriate. Be sure to label your graphic organizer appropriately.

**Directions**

Now you will write a paper in response to a writing prompt. First, read the prompt in the box below.

Then use the separate paper your teacher has given you for your prewriting activity (such as brainstorming, listing, freewriting, clustering, mapping, or drawing).

After you finish your prewriting activity, write your first draft on the separate paper your teacher has given you. Look back at your prewriting activity for ideas.

## Writing Prompt

The folk tale "Ashputtle" is a variation on the "Cinderella" story. Write a paper in which you select a well-known story and retell it in your own words. The story could come from literature, film, or even television. Before you tell your own version, explain where you first read or learned about the story.

NAME _____   DATE _____

# *WRITING*

## Directions

Now you have time to revise your draft. Reread your draft and think about the Writer's Checklist below. Check every box that makes a true statement about your draft.

## Writer's Checklist

☐ My paper has a beginning, middle, and end.

☐ My paper uses paragraphing appropriately.

☐ My paper flows smoothly from one idea to another.

☐ My paper stays on the topic.

☐ My paper includes details and examples.

☐ My paper uses precise and vivid language.

☐ My paper includes a variety of sentence structures.

☐ My paper includes correct grammar usage, punctuation, capitalization, and spelling.

For every box you did not check, make the necessary revisions on your draft before you write your final copy.

## Narcissus

(page 828)

**1** Explain why Hera punished Echo. Use details and/or examples from the story to support your explanation.

_____

_____

_____

_____

**2** The word *narcissism* refers to the act of greatly admiring yourself. Explain why you think there is a connection between this modern word and the Greek myth of Narcissus. Use details and/or examples from the story to support your explanation.

_____

_____

_____

_____

**3** Explain why Aphrodite punished Narcissus. Use details and/or examples from the story to support your explanation.

_____

_____

_____

_____

**4** How was Narcissus's pain similar to the pain that Echo felt? Use details and/or examples from the story to support your answer.

_____

_____

_____

_____

NAME _____ DATE _____

# Young Arthur (page 832)

**1** Explain why young Arthur was sent away to be raised in Sir Ector's house. Use details and/or examples from the story to support your explanation.

_____

_____

_____

_____

**2** There are many similarities and differences between Arthur and his foster brother, Kay. In the space below, construct a graphic organizer that compares Arthur with Kay. Use details and information from the story in your answer.

Your graphic organizer may be a chart, graph, diagram, drawing, cluster, web, mind map, or other organizer you feel is appropriate. Be sure to label your graphic organizer appropriately.

**3** Explain why Arthur pulled the sword from the stone the first time. Use details and/or examples from the story to support your explanation.

_____

_____

_____

_____

**4** Arthur fled because he thought that he had committed a crime, but he was actually innocent. Explain why he misunderstood the excitement over the sword. Use details and/or examples from the story to support your explanation.

_____

_____

_____

## Lazy Peter and His Three-Cornered Hat  (page 836)

**1** A con, or confidence game, often involves a thief who earns another person's trust in some way. How does Lazy Peter earn the trust and confidence of the rich farmer? Use details and/or examples from the story to support your answer.

_____

_____

_____

_____

**2** Lazy Peter told three people that he would be wearing his hat three different ways. He said that the way he wore his hat would be the way that he could be recognized. Complete the chart below by describing the three ways Peter wore his hat in front of the three different characters.

| Story Character | The Way Peter Wore His Hat for Him |
|---|---|
| 1. Stand Owner | 1. |
| 2. Druggist | 2. |
| 3. Priest | 3. |

**3** Explain why you think that Lazy Peter visited the priest last. Use details and/or examples from the story to support your explanation.

_____

_____

_____

_____

**4** Explain how Lazy Peter and the rich farmer are similar. Use details and/or examples from the story to support your explanation.

_____

_____

_____

_____

**1** Explain why Phaëthon goes to visit Apollo. Use details and/or examples from the story to support your explanation.

_____

_____

_____

_____

**2** This myth includes the names of several constellations, or star formations. List <u>four</u> of those constellations.

1. _____

2. _____

3. _____

4. _____

**3** Explain how Phaëthon died. Use details and/or examples from the story to support your explanation.

_____

_____

_____

_____

**4** Why did Apollo not stop Phaëthon from driving the sun chariot? Use details and/or examples from the story to support your answer.

_____

_____

_____

_____

NAME _____ DATE _____

## The Force of Luck

*(page 845)*

**1** Explain what happens to the first two hundred dollars that was given to the miller. Use details and/or examples from the story to support your explanation.

_____

_____

_____

_____

**2** Explain why the piece of lead was not "worthless," as one man had described it. Use details and/or examples from the story to support your explanation.

_____

_____

_____

_____

**3** Explain why the jeweler and his wife first offered only fifty dollars for the diamond and then later offered one hundred thousand dollars for it. Use details and/or examples from the story to support your explanation.

_____

_____

_____

_____

**4** Which point of view does this story support—that a person needs luck or money in order to be prosperous? Use details and/or examples from the story to support your answer.

_____

_____

_____

_____

NAME _____ DATE _____

# Brother Coyote and Brother Cricket (page 853)

**1** Both Brother Coyote and Brother Cricket assembled armies. Complete the chart below by listing <u>five</u> members of Brother Coyote's army and <u>five</u> members of Brother Cricket's army. One has been completed.

Members of Brother Coyote's Army     Members of Brother Cricket's Army

| Fox | Horseflies |
|---|---|
| 1. | 1. |
| 2. | 2. |
| 3. | 3. |
| 4. | 4. |
| 5. | 5. |

**2** Brother Coyote says, "When nature offers itself, it is fair for nature to accept." In the context of this fable, what is the meaning of this phrase? Use details and/or examples from the story to support your answer.

_____

_____

_____

_____

**3** When a writer gives human qualities to an animal, object, or idea, this is called personification. Name <u>three</u> examples of personification in this story.

1. _____

2. _____

3. _____

**4** A fable often teaches a simple lesson, or moral. Explain the moral of this fable. Use details and/or examples from the story to support your explanation.

_____

_____

_____

_____

NAME _____  DATE _____

# How Odin Lost His Eye

*(page 858)*

**1** Explain why Odin left his throne to travel down to earth. Use details and/or examples from the story to support your answer.

_____

_____

_____

_____

**2** Explain why Mimir warned Odin about drinking out of the well. Use details and/or examples from the story to support your explanation.

_____

_____

_____

_____

**3** Explain how Odin's son, Balder, plays a role in this myth. Use details and/or examples from the story to support your answer.

_____

_____

_____

_____

**4** A theme is the message about life or human nature that is conveyed by a literary work. What is the theme of this myth? Use details and/or examples from the story to support your explanation.

_____

_____

_____

_____

NAME _____ DATE _____

# Pumpkin Seed and the Snake (page 861)

**1** Explain why the huge boulder kept disappearing and then returning to the family's garden. Use details and/or examples from the story to support your answer.

_____

_____

_____

_____

**2** Explain why Pumpkin Vine refused to open the door to the family's house, but her younger sister, Pumpkin Seed, agreed to open the door. Use details and/or examples from the story to support your explanation.

_____

_____

_____

_____

**3** The story contains a scene in which Pumpkin Seed plays with colorful bubbles in a stream. In the space below, draw a diagram of this scene.

Your diagram should include Pumpkin Seed and the stream. Use your imagination, but pay close attention to the story's descriptive details. Be sure to label your diagram appropriately.

**4** How does Pumpkin Seed know that the young, handsome man was also the snake? Use details and/or examples from the story to support your explanation.

_____

_____

_____

_____

NAME _____ DATE _____

## Kelfala's Secret Something (page 866)

**1** This folk tale uses examples of figurative language, including the simile and the metaphor. A simile is a comparison that uses the signal word *like* or *as*. A metaphor is a direct comparison with no signal words. Complete the chart below by listing <u>two</u> more similes and <u>two</u> more metaphors from the story.

FIGURATIVE LANGUAGE IN "KELFALA'S SECRET SOMETHING"

| Simile (Using *like* or *as*) | Metaphor |
|---|---|
| **"Kelfala howled like a ruffled owl."** | **"He rolled himself into a ball."** |
| 1. | 1. |
| 2. | 2. |

**2** Explain why the young men in the village teased Wambuna when she was in her garden. Use details and/or examples from the story to support your explanation.

_____

_____

_____

_____

## *Kelfala's Secret Something* *continued*

**3** Explain why Shortie Bumpie and Longie Tallie felt that Wambuna should not marry Kelfala and Kelfala alone. Use details and/or examples from the story to support your explanation.

_____

_____

_____

_____

**4** Imagine what would happen next in the story. If the story were to continue, explain what you think Kelfala would do next. Use details and/or examples from the story to support your answer.

_____

_____

_____

_____

**Directions**

Now you will write a paper in response to a writing prompt. First, read the prompt in the box below.

Then use the separate paper your teacher has given you for your prewriting activity (such as brainstorming, listing, freewriting, clustering, mapping, or drawing).

After you finish your prewriting activity, write your first draft on the separate paper your teacher has given you. Look back at your prewriting activity for ideas.

## Writing Prompt

> Every person has at least one talent, characteristic, or personality trait that makes him or her unique. Write a paper about something that makes you different from everybody else. Explain how this quality makes you a unique person.

### Directions

Now you have time to revise your draft. Reread your draft and think about the Writer's Checklist below. Check every box that makes a true statement about your draft.

## Writer's Checklist

☐ My paper has a beginning, middle, and end.

☐ My paper uses paragraphing appropriately.

☐ My paper flows smoothly from one idea to another.

☐ My paper stays on the topic.

☐ My paper includes details and examples.

☐ My paper uses precise and vivid language.

☐ My paper includes a variety of sentence structures.

☐ My paper includes correct grammar usage, punctuation, capitalization, and spelling.

For every box you did not check, make the necessary revisions on your draft before you write your final copy.

## Seventh Grade (page 20)

1.   Example of a top score-point response:

   1.   Victor has a crush on Teresa, and he knows that she is also taking the French course.

   2.   Victor thought he might like to travel to France one day because the weather is much cooler there than in Fresno, where he lives.

   Other possible responses:

   •   France seemed interesting to Victor because it had rivers, churches, and "fair-skinned people everywhere."

   •   Victor already spoke English and Spanish, so this would be an opportunity to learn a new language.

   **Content Standard(s): 2**
   **Process Standard(s): 3.5**

2.   Examples of top score-point responses:

   •   Michael thinks that girls will be more attracted to him if he wears a scowl.

   •   Michael thinks that a scowl will make him more handsome and perhaps more intriguing.

   •   Michael had noticed that male models in a fashion magazine often scowled, so he concluded that a scowl would make him more appealing to girls.

   **Content Standard(s): 2**
   **Process Standard(s): 3.5**

3.   Example of top score-point response:

   •   Victor is embarrassed because he became very nervous and tongue-tied when he tried to speak French. He could only mumble. Teresa, however, was impressed because she thought that Victor had done well in class.

   **Content Standard(s): 2**
   **Process Standard(s): 1.6**

4.   Example of top score-point response:

   •   Victor has a crush on Teresa and he hopes that he can see her outside and possibly even talk to her. He has liked Teresa since they took "catechism classes at St. Theresa's" when they were younger.

   **Content Standard(s): 2**
   **Process Standard(s): 3.5**

## *Thank You, M'am* (page 29)

1.  Examples of top score-point responses:

Setting and Time of Day        Story Detail

| It is nighttime. | "Goodnight! Behave yourself, boy!" |
|---|---|
| 1. Mrs. Jones lives in a boarding house. | "The boy could hear the other roomers laughing and talking in the large house." |
| 2. The characters live in a city. | There is "a large kitchenette-furnished room at the rear of the house." |
| 3. It is late at night. | "It was about eleven o'clock at night." |

**Content Standard(s): 2**
**Process Standard(s): 3.5**

2.  Examples of top score-point responses:

- She feels sorry for the boy. Mrs. Jones knows that Roger must be hungry or very desperate if he is out on the streets trying to steal someone's purse.

- Earlier in her life, Mrs. Jones also did some bad things, and she wants to teach Roger a lesson. She does not want him to make the same mistakes that she did.

- She wants to shame the boy and try to steer him away from the life of a petty thief. She thinks it is wrong to steal.

**Content Standard(s): 2**
**Process Standard(s): 3.5**

3.  Think about the two characters, Roger and Mrs. Jones, from the short story "Thank You, M'am." In the space below, construct a graphic organizer that shows how they are similar and how they are different. Use details and information from the story in your answer.

Your graphic organizer may be a chart, graph, diagram, drawing, cluster, web, mind map, or other organizer you feel is appropriate. Be sure to label your graphic organizer appropriately.

Example(s):

| Differences Between Roger and Mrs. Jones |
|---|
| 1. Roger is a teenager, but Mrs. Jones is much older. |
| 2. Roger is dirty, but Mrs. Jones is very presentable. |
| 3. Roger does not have a job, but Mrs. Jones works at a beauty shop. |

| Similarities Between Roger and Mrs. Jones |
|---|
| 1. Roger and Mrs. Jones live in the same city, and perhaps even in the same neighborhood. |
| 2. Both characters spend a lot of time alone. Mrs. Jones lives alone, and Roger says that there is nobody home at his house. |
| 3. Both characters have known what it feels like to be so desperate that you would consider doing something wrong, such as stealing. |

**Content Standard(s): 2, 4**
**Process Standard(s): 1.6, 1.8**

### *If I Can Stop One Heart from Breaking* (page 33)

1. Example of top score-point response:

   - The narrator is very generous and caring. Her main goals in life are to help people and animals who need assistance.

     **Content Standard(s): 2**
     **Process Standard(s): 3.5**

2. Examples of top score-point responses:

   - Mrs. Jones wants to help Roger. Instead of simply letting him go after he tries to steal her purse, she forces him to spend time with her. She feeds him, allows him to clean up, and gives him some money. She seems pleased to help the boy. The narrator of the poem also wants to help people. The poem suggests that helping people is what gives the narrator satisfaction. The narrator says that if she can ease someone's pain or help a struggling robin into its nest, then she will not "live in vain." In other words, her life has been worthwhile.

   - Mrs. Jones and the narrator of the poem both go out of their way to help other people. Both characters are very concerned about the welfare of others. Mrs. Jones helps a boy named Roger, and the narrator of the poem even helps a little bird.

     **Content Standard(s): 2**
     **Process Standard(s): 1.6**

### *Names/Nombres* (page 37)

1. Example of a top score-point response:

   1. Judy
   2. Judith
   3. Juliet

   Other possible responses:

   - Jules
   - Hey Jude
   - Alcatraz
     **Content Standard(s): 3**
     **Process Standard(s): 3.5**

2. Examples of top score-point responses:

   - Julia's relatives had complicated names. There were many, many relatives, and the relationships between them were often confusing to even Julia herself. It was a real challenge to explain all those relationships.

   - Julia's relatives were different from her friends' parents. They spoke a different language, and their styles of dress were different. Their mannerisms seemed quite different, at least in Julia's eyes.

     **Content Standard(s): 3**
     **Process Standard(s): 3.5**

3. Examples of top score-point responses:

- Julia's friends thought that her name sounded exotic. It was unusual because it was so long, compared to the full names of most people.

- Julia's friends liked to hear her say her name because it was incredibly long. According to Dominican custom, Julia's name included her middle name and her mother's and father's surnames for four generations back: Julia Altagracia María Teresa Álvarez Tavares Perello Espaillat Julia Pérez Rochet González.

    **Content Standard(s): 3**
    **Process Standard(s): 3.5**

4. Examples of top score-point responses:

- Julia was given a portable typewriter so that she could pursue her love of writing.

- Julia's relatives knew that she loved literature and that she enjoyed writing poems and stories. This gift showed that the family was supportive of her creative expression. The family predicted that Julia would become well-known. The prediction came true because Julia Alvarez is now a famous author.

    **Content Standard(s): 3**
    **Process Standard(s): 3.5**

## *Zebra* (page 46)

1. Example of top score-point response:

- Mr. Wilson had served in Vietnam with a good friend named Leon. Mr. Wilson wanted to give the drawing to Leon as a present. Mr. Wilson "gave" the gift to Leon by taking it to the Vietnam Veterans Memorial in Washington, D.C. Leon's name is on The Wall there because he is one of the soldiers who died in Vietnam.

    **Content Standard(s): 2**
    **Process Standard(s): 3.5**

2. Examples of top score-point responses:

- By reading over the description of the places where Zebra liked to run, it seems like he was hit when he ran into traffic.

- Zebra was probably hit by a car or truck. He loved to run, but one day he ran down a hill so quickly that he accidentally ran into moving traffic. His mother had warned him not to run so fast that he wouldn't be able to stop at one particular corner.

    **Content Standard(s): 2**
    **Process Standard(s): 3.5**

3. Example(s):

- Student drawings should include a depiction of Mr. Wilson and an appropriate caption.

    **Content Standard(s): 2, 4**
    **Process Standard(s): 2.1**

## *The Rider* (page 61)

1. Examples of top score-point responses:

   - The narrator is talking about the sensation of overcoming a feeling of loneliness. Loneliness can be defeated by roller-skating or bicycling. The narrator compares the sensation to floating free in a cloud of flowers.

   - The narrator no longer feels weighed down by loneliness. The narrator feels that loneliness can be left behind, like a person who is "panting behind you on some street corner."

   **Content Standard(s): 2**
   **Process Standard(s): 3.5**

2. Example of top score-point response:

   - The narrator is riding a bicycle, "pedaling hard down King William Street." The narrator is also remembering something that a boy once said about roller-skating. The narrator wonders if that boy's comment could also apply to bicycle riding.

   **Content Standard(s): 2**
   **Process Standard(s): 3.5**

## *Offerings at The Wall* (page 65)

1. Examples of top score-point responses:

   - People bring objects and letters to the memorial as a way to honor the soldiers who died in Vietnam. Like flowers carried to a cemetery, these small objects are meant to honor the soldiers who have died.

   - People take these objects to The Wall because it helps them to remember their loved ones. Giving these offerings makes people feel connected to their departed loved ones. These gifts are tributes.

   **Content Standard(s): 3**
   **Process Standard(s): 3.5**

2. Examples of top score-point responses:

   - Each gift is unique, so what would seem odd or unusual to one person would not seem odd to another person. A letter or photograph seems typical, but a Popsicle stick seems really unusual to me. Perhaps the soldier really loved Popsicles, or perhaps it was a very old stick from a treat that was eaten long ago.

   - Playing cards seem like an unusual gift. Of course, a dead soldier cannot "use" any of the gifts, but the thought is very important. Giving a offering at the wall helps people to remember the courage, service, and sacrifice of these soldiers.

   **Content Standard(s): 3**
   **Process Standard(s): 1.6**

3. Example(s):

   - Student diagrams should include the memorial and at least one offering. The diagrams should also be labeled.

   **Content Standard(s): 3, 4**
   **Process Standard(s): 1.8**

## A Crush (page 68)

1. Example of top score-point response:

   • A delivery person accidentally delivered a box of flower seeds to Ernie's house. He loved the photos on the packages. After Ernie moved into a group home, he met Jack and starting planting his flower seeds.

   **Content Standard(s): 2**
   **Process Standard(s): 3.5**

2. Examples of top score-point responses:

   | Ernie's Flowers | Jack's Plants |
   |---|---|

   | Zinnias | Red radishes |
   |---|---|
   | 1. Cornflowers | 1. Eggplant |
   | 2. Marigolds | 2. Tomatoes |
   | Other possibilities:<br>• Nasturtiums<br>• Asters<br>• Four-o'clocks<br>• Violets | Other possibility:<br>• Squash |

   **Content Standard(s): 2**
   **Process Standard(s): 1.6**

3. Examples of top score-point responses:

   • Dolores has a tattoo. Dolores has a great knowledge of machinery and hardware supplies. Dolores does not wear clothes that are considered fashionable.

   • Dolores, unlike many of her female customers, does not wear makeup. For Dolores, it seems that doing her job well is far more important that dressing fashionably or having a stylish haircut.

   **Content Standard(s): 2**
   **Process Standard(s): 1.6**

4. Examples of top score-point responses:

   • Dolores has never met Ernie, who loves her from a distance. There is no way that she could know the identity of her "secret admirer" because she has never even met him.

   • Ernie delivers the flowers to Dolores very early in the morning, before the hardware store opens. Dolores probably does not want to spend the effort to "spy" on the hardware store in the early hours in order to find out who is delivering the flowers. Dolores does not know the flower giver's identity because he is a stranger to her.

   **Content Standard(s): 2**
   **Process Standard(s): 3.5**

5.  Example of top score-point response:

- Jack wants to help Ernie grow flowers indoors. Jack knows that Ernie enjoys gardening, so he has come up with a plan that will allow Ernie to grow violets indoors using artificial light instead of sunlight. Most flowers cannot grow outside during a cold winter.

    **Content Standard(s): 2**
    **Process Standard(s): 3.5**

### *Eleanor Roosevelt* (page 87)

1.  Examples of top score-point responses:

Difficult Things About Eleanor Roosevelt's Childhood

| |
| --- |
| 1. Her father was an alcoholic who went away to live in a sanitarium. |
| 2. She had to endure much grief because her mother, father, and brother all died within a span of eighteen months. |
| 3. She had to live with Grandmother Hall, who often neglected her. |
| Other possibilities:<br>• Her mother was cool and distant toward her.<br>• She was teased about her appearance.<br>• Her cousin Alice seemed to delight in making her feel uncomfortable. |

**Content Standard(s): 3**
**Process Standard(s): 3.5**

2.  Example of top score-point response:

- Theodore Roosevelt was Eleanor's uncle. Eleanor's father, Elliott, was the younger brother of Theodore. Franklin was Eleanor's fifth cousin, and he also became her husband.

    **Content Standard(s): 3**
    **Process Standard(s): 3.5**

3.  Examples of top score-point responses:

- Eleanor was committed to the idea of social change. She urged President Roosevelt to pass laws that would help people who were not being treated fairly. She fought against racism and intolerance. Eleanor Roosevelt fought for equal pay for women. She encouraged the president to support legislation that helped impoverished students to stay in school.

- Since President Roosevelt was disabled, Eleanor was better able to travel around the nation. She traveled all over the country, speaking to needy people and then reporting her information back to the president. She helped the president to "stay in touch" with the concerns of regular people. She helped him to understand exactly what Americans had to go through during the Great Depression.

    **Content Standard(s): 3**
    **Process Standard(s): 3.5**

4.  Example of top score-point response:

- As a child, Eleanor was formal, distant, and shy. As an adult, she was a warm person who could relate to practically any type of person. As a child, Eleanor was very insecure. As an adult, she was very powerful and persuasive. It is hard to believe that a child who was so shy could become a great leader.

    **Content Standard(s): 3**
    **Process Standard(s): 1.6**

### *The Autobiography of Eleanor Roosevelt* (page 97)

1.  Examples of top score-point responses:

    -   The biography is written in the third person, but the autobiography is written in the first person. Eleanor begins a lot of sentences with the word "I."

    -   Jacobs' writing does not use vocabulary words that have the same level of difficulty and complexity as Roosevelt's autobiography. In a way, Jacobs' writing style is easier for some readers to understand.

    -   Jacobs does not deal with Eleanor Roosevelt's internal feelings as much as Roosevelt herself does. You could say that Roosevelt's writing is more accurate because she is the person who lived through these events and felt those feelings.
        **Content Standard(s): 3**
        **Process Standard(s): 1.6**

### *No Ordinary Time* (page 97)

1.  Examples of top score-point responses:

    -   Eleanor was persuasive. She was a charismatic person who had a great deal of influence on her husband. She could convince her husband, the president, to take certain positions on key issues. Eleanor influenced his political decisions.

    -   Eleanor was energetic and insistent. She was determined and compassionate. She helped the president to see things from her point of view.

        **Content Standard(s): 3**
        **Process Standard(s): 1.6**

### *Homeless* (page 101)

1.  Example of a top score-point response:

    1.  A room painted blue
    2.  A plastic dish drying rack

    Other possible responses:

    -   A leaky roof
    -   A drawer that holds the spoons
    -   A window "to look out upon the world"

        **Content Standard(s): 3**
        **Process Standard(s): 3.5**

2.  Examples of top score-point responses:

    -   This photograph is special because it is of the house where the woman once lived. This photograph probably holds happy memories of when life was better for this woman.

    -   The woman's self-identity and self-esteem are probably wrapped up in her ideas about the house. The woman shows the photograph to the narrator to prove that she has not always been homeless.

        **Content Standard(s): 3**
        **Process Standard(s): 3.5**

3. Examples of top score-point responses:

- The main idea is that homeless people are individuals. Each homeless person should be treated with respect. Too often, when people talk about "the homeless," they forget that they are talking about specific individuals.

- Having a home is one of the most important things in life. It does not have to be fancy, but it does have to have something that makes a person feel like he or she is at home. Homeless people were not always homeless. A homeless person once had a home, and it is a terrible feeling of sorrow to know that you no longer have a home to go to.

**Content Standard(s): 3**
**Process Standard(s): 3.5**

4. **Content Standard(s): 3**
**Process Standard(s): 3.5**

### Bums in the Attic from The House on Mango Street (page 105)

1. Example of top score-point response:

- The narrator is ashamed of her relatives, but she does not want to admit it to them. She does not like looking at expensive homes that her family cannot afford. These trips to the neighborhood where her father works as a gardener now make her feel uncomfortable.

**Content Standard(s): 2**
**Process Standard(s): 3.5**

2. Example of top score-point response:

- The narrator says that when she has her own house, she will invite bums to sleep in the attic. She says that she will do this because she knows "how it is to be without a house." The narrator feels that she will not forget her difficult past when she does find herself living in a house.

**Content Standard(s): 2**
**Process Standard(s): 3.5**

3. Example of top score-point response:

- Both narrators show compassion for those people who are homeless. The narrator of "Homeless" encourages the reader to remember that homeless people are all individuals who once had homes. The narrator of "Bums in the Attic" would like to help homeless people by offering to let them sleep in her home.

**Content Standard(s): 2, 3**
**Process Standard(s): 1.6**

### The War of the Wall (page 109)

1.  Examples of top score-point responses:

| Location and Time Period | Story Detail |
|---|---|
| **A city not far from a rural area** | **The family takes a car trip to visit Grandma, who lives on a farm.** |
| 1. A city, but not one that is close to New York City | The family marvels at television images of New York City. |
| 2. The late 1960s or early 1970s | The narrator remembers the beginning of integration in the early 1960s. |
| 3. The setting is in an inner-city. | A painter creates a mural on a wall on Taliaferro Street. |

Other possibilities:

- The story is set on Taliaferro Street in a city.
- The story is set in the South; the mother makes a comment about the painter being "from the North."
- The story is set in a time period after the rise to national prominence of Malcolm X and Dr. Martin Luther King, Jr., who are both depicted in the mural.

**Content Standard(s): 2**
**Process Standard(s): 3.5**

2.  Example of top score-point response:

- Jimmy Lyons was a soldier who died while fighting in the Vietnam War. Jimmy used to live in the narrator's neighborhood. The narrator chiseled Jimmy's name on the wall as a tribute. Jimmy's cousin is the painter who creates a mural in his honor for the people of Taliaferro Street.

**Content Standard(s): 2**
**Process Standard(s): 3.5**

3.  Examples of top score-point responses:

- Lou and the narrator initially dislike the painter because they feel like she is invading their neighborhood. She seems foreign and strange to them. She comes from New York state and eats different foods than they do. She doesn't seem to want to talk to anybody.

- Lou and the narrator do not like her because she has come to change things. They like the wall the way that it is, and they don't want her to paint it. They don't want her around because, in their minds, that wall belongs to the people of Taliaferro Street, and she shouldn't be touching it.

**Content Standard(s): 2**
**Process Standard(s): 3.5**

4.  Example of top score-point response:

- The other figures in the mural look like real people who live in the neighborhood, such as Frieda Morris, Hattie Morris, the narrator, Lou, and the narrator's father. The painter incorporated images of people who live on Taliaferro Street and the surrounding area.

**Content Standard(s): 2**
**Process Standard(s): 3.5**

## *Song of Myself* (page 117)

1. Examples of top score-point responses:

   • The narrator is cheerful and content. This is a person who is very happy with who he is. The narrator is happy with himself, and he doesn't care whether or not he has fame.

   • The narrator uses the words "cheerfully" and "cheerfulness" to describe how he doesn't care whether he "comes into [his] own" now or in the future. The narrator is an introspective sort of person who explores the "world" that is his own mind and soul.

   **Content Standard(s): 2**
   **Process Standard(s): 3.5**

## *Rikki-tikki-tavi* (page 121)

1. Examples of top score-point responses:

   • Nag knows that Teddy's father used a gun to kill the snake Karait. Nag also knows that Teddy's father will not be carrying a gun when he walks into the bathroom to bathe.

   • Nag is hiding in a place where Teddy's father will not see him. Nag's plan is to surprise the man and strike him when he walks into the bathroom. If he is sleepy when he walks into the bathroom, he will be particularly vulnerable to Nag's attack.

   **Content Standard(s): 2**
   **Process Standard(s): 3.5**

2. Example of top score-point response:

   • Teddy's mother does not think this is a good idea. She fears that the mongoose may bite Teddy. Teddy's father, however, thinks it is a good idea because the mongoose can protect the boy from snakes. Teddy's father comments that the mongoose is an even better defender than a bloodhound. Teddy's father is much more familiar with mongooses than his wife is. At one point, he says, "All mongooses are like that." This shows that he is very familiar with the animal.

   **Content Standard(s): 2**
   **Process Standard(s): 1.6**

3. Examples of top score-point responses:

   Animal Character     Human Quality or Characteristic

   | **Nagaina** | **sneaky** |
   |---|---|
   | 1. Nag | strong; vicious; wicked |
   | 2. Rikki-tikki | brave; noble; protective |
   | 3. Chuchundra | scared; sensitive; weak; emotional |

   **Content Standard(s): 2**
   **Process Standard(s): 1.6**

4. Examples of top score-point responses:

- Rikki-tikki does not like Darzee. He calls the bird "a stupid tuft of feathers." He becomes angry with Darzee because he feels that the bird is too focused upon singing his happy song. He wants Darzee to shut up and pay attention.

- Rikki-tikki becomes annoyed because Darzee won't answer his question about the location of Nagaina. Rikki-tikki tries to get Darzee to help him, but the bird just keeps on singing the praises of the mongoose. Darzee's wife, a "sensible bird," did help Rikki-tikki by distracting Nagaina.

**Content Standard(s): 2**
**Process Standard(s): 3.5**

### *Primal Compassion* (page 138)

1. Examples of top score-point responses:

- Bob is saying that humans should be compassionate creatures. If gorillas—animals that are less advanced than people—can be compassionate, then shouldn't humans also be capable of such compassion? Binti the gorilla provides an example of how we should all act.

- Bob is saying that the story of Binti provides an example of how people should behave and relate to other creatures. The gorilla helped save a boy. Bob feels that the lesson to be learned is that we should all be compassionate to all people and animals.

**Content Standard(s): 3**
**Process Standard(s): 3.5**

2. Examples of top score-point responses:

- Eric did not want Bob to photograph the boy because he felt it would be wrong to benefit from another person's suffering. Eric thought that during an emergency situation, it was a cruel act to photograph what was going on. He thought it was insensitive. Eric thought that everyone's first concern should be for the boy's safety and well-being.

- Eric did not want his father to gain any money or fame from photographing a tragic event. The boy could have even died in that horrible situation. The family agreed that Bob would only share the photographs if the boy recovered. The boy did recover.

**Content Standard(s): 3**
**Process Standard(s): 3.5**

3.    Example(s):

| Differences Between Rikki-tikki and Binti Jua | |
|---|---|
| mongoose | gorilla |
| lives in a house | lives in a zoo |
| enemy is a snake | has no real enemies in the zoo |
| male | female |
| kills a snake | growls at another gorilla |

| Similarities Between Rikki-tikki and Binti Jua |
|---|
| Both are protective of humans. |
| Both communicate with other animals. |
| Both face very dramatic situations. |
| Both showed human-like behavior. |

Content Standard(s): 2, 3, 4
Process Standard(s): 1.6, 1.8

## *Dirk the Protector* (page 143)

1.    Example of top score-point response:

- After work one day, the boy wandered into a dark alcove off an alley. There, by accident, he met the alley dog Dirk. As he was climbing down a fire escape, he almost stepped on Dirk. The boy gave the dog some hamburger, Dirk saved him from the bullies, and the boy and the dog became companions.

  Content Standard(s): 2
  Process Standard(s): 3.5

2.    Examples of top score-point responses:

- Happy Santum was a bully and a thug who enjoyed tormenting the narrator. He was also a thief. He seemed to be an angry and cruel person, so "Happy" is not an appropriate nickname for him.

- "Happy" is a good name for someone who is usually in a good mood, not someone who enjoys beating up other people.

  Content Standard(s): 2
  Process Standard(s): 3.5

3.    Example of a top score-point response:

  1.    Setting pins at a bowling alley
  2.    Selling newspapers

  Other possible response:
  - Working on a farm

    Content Standard(s): 2
    Process Standard(s): 3.5

4.    Examples of top score-point responses:

- Dirk found a new home on a farm, and he seemed very happy there. He left behind his life in the city to become a country dog.

- Dirk became a guard dog for a herd of sheep. The narrator worked for a farmer named Olaf, and when the summer ended, Dirk stayed on the farm. Dirk seemed to enjoy guarding the sheep.

  **Content Standard(s): 2**
  **Process Standard(s): 3.5**

5.    Example of top score-point response:

- One of the regular bowlers rolled a perfect game. In celebration, he "bought the pit boys hamburgers and Cokes." A bowler bought this rare treat for the narrator.

  **Content Standard(s): 2**
  **Process Standard(s): 3.5**

### *O. Henry* (page 150)

1.    Examples of top score-point responses:

- William Sydney Porter may have committed a crime that he was ashamed of. So he changed his name. He didn't want to tell anybody about this toward the end of his life.

- While working as a bank teller, William Sydney Porter was accused of stealing money to finance his humorous weekly newspaper. He later served time in jail. After his release from prison, Porter "left behind his shameful identity as a convict." Ashamed of his past, he changed his name to O. Henry.

  **Content Standard(s): 3**
  **Process Standard(s): 3.5**

2.    Example of top score-point response:

- During O. Henry's day, doctors had not found effective medicines or treatments for treating tuberculosis. Three of O. Henry's relatives died from tuberculosis, and he lived in fear of getting this horrible disease.

  **Content Standard(s): 3**
  **Process Standard(s): 3.5**

### *After Twenty Years* (page 154)

1.    Examples of top score-point responses:

- The reader does not realize that the uniformed officer is Jimmy, the man that "Silky" Bob is supposed to meet. Bob doesn't realize this, either. The reader (and Bob) only discover this at the very end, when Jimmy's note is revealed.

- You don't think that the police officer is the guy that Bob is looking for. Also, you don't realize that Jimmy recognized Bob as a criminal. These things are not revealed until the very end, which gives the story a surprise ending. It does not turn out the way you expect it will.

  **Content Standard(s): 2**
  **Process Standard(s): 3.5**

2.  Example of top score-point response:

    • Bob has a lot of money. He wears a scarf pin with a large diamond, and he carries a handsome watch that is covered with diamonds. Bob probably got rich in the West. He probably made this money dishonestly because he is wanted by the police. There is a warrant out for his arrest.

    **Content Standard(s): 2**
    **Process Standard(s): 3.5**

3.  Example of top score-point response:

    • The two men have changed since they were teenagers. Jimmy became a police officer. Jimmy never left New York City. Bob, however, traveled west and became a thief. As Bob ironically states, each of the men now has his "destiny worked out."

    **Content Standard(s): 2**
    **Process Standard(s): 1.6**

4.  Examples of top score-point responses:

    • The patrolman wrote, "Somehow I couldn't do it myself." Since Bob was a childhood friend, the patrolman couldn't go through the emotional ordeal of arresting the man.

    • Since Bob was an old childhood buddy, Jimmy could not make the arrest himself. He did, however, want the man arrested, so he got a "plainclothes man to do the job." It would have been difficult for Jimmy to arrest someone whom he had known as a teenager.

    **Content Standard(s): 2**
    **Process Standard(s): 3.5**

## *A Retrieved Reformation* (page 163)

1.  Examples of top score-point responses:

    • Ben Price has decided not to arrest Jimmy Valentine. Price realizes that Valentine is willing to expose his burglary skills to his family in order to save the little girl. So, instead of arresting Valentine, Price decides to protect the secret identity.

    • At the end of this story, both Ben Price and Jimmy Valentine seem to have a change of heart. Valentine reveals his thief's tools to his family. This could easily lead to a revelation of his true identity as a thief. Instead of arresting Valentine, Price decides to let him go free. Price perhaps realizes that Valentine is not such a bad person after all.

    **Content Standard(s): 2**
    **Process Standard(s): 3.5**

2.  Example of top score-point response:

    • This letter shows that Jimmy has had a change of heart. He wants to turn his back on a life of crime. He wants to hand over his tools to an old friend. He has decided to stop cracking safes.

    **Content Standard(s): 2**
    **Process Standard(s): 3.5**

3.      Examples of top score-point responses:

- The author strongly hints that Jimmy committed these crimes. The robberies happened right after Jimmy was released from prison. The author presents this information in a way that leads the reader to the conclusion that Jimmy did it. It was not just a coincidence that the robberies happened right after a notorious safecracker was released from jail.

- Ben Price investigated this series of robberies. He said that these crime scenes had "Dandy Jim Valentine's autograph." In other words, the safes had been broken into in the same way that Jimmy had broken into other safes. Price said, "He's got the only clamps that can do it." Price knows that Jimmy is the only person who owns the tools to crack a safe in a certain way.

**Content Standard(s): 2**
**Process Standard(s): 3.5**

4.      Example of top score-point response:

- The author doesn't make it exactly clear what Jimmy's motivation is. He may be using a false name because he wants to rob the bank. He may, however, be using a new name because he wants to start a new, honest life with a fresh identity. Perhaps Jimmy truly does want to become a law-abiding citizen. Regardless of his motivation, he cannot use the name "Jimmy Valentine" because that is the name of a career criminal.

**Content Standard(s): 2**
**Process Standard(s): 3.5**

### From Short Story to Big Screen (page 173)

1.      Examples of top score-point responses:

- Audiences like to see stories of Good vs. Evil. This is why Westerns, gangster movies, and professional wrestling are popular. In the story "A Retrieved Reformation," the reader feels complicated emotions. You're not sure whether or not to be happy about the idea that Jimmy Valentine might get arrested. In a way, now that he has reformed himself, it seems okay that he was not arrested. The tug between the forces of Good and Evil is what makes gangster/detective movies popular.

- These type of movies and plays are popular because audiences like to watch characters who have to fight with their strength and their intelligence. It is fun to watch (or read along) as the detective is closing in on Jimmy Valentine. These types of stories have a lot of suspense because you're not sure whether the criminal will get away with it. Audiences are fascinated by characters who seem to have no respect for the law. At first, when Jimmy is cracking safes, he seems to show no remorse. Later, he decides to change his ways. At the end, it looks like he is going to be arrested, but the detective lets him go free.

**Content Standard(s): 3**
**Process Standard(s): 3.5**

### *The Pasture* (page 196)

1.  Example of a top score-point response:

    1.  watching the water clear out of a pasture
    2.  watching a mother cow lick a young calf

    Other possible responses:

    *   raking leaves out of the pasture
    *   taking a walk or doing chores in the countryside

        **Content Standard(s): 2**
        **Process Standard(s): 3.5**

2.  Examples of top score-point responses:

    *   These lines, which say, "I shan't be gone long.—You come too," give the poem a warm, happy mood. The narrator is a friendly person, and he's talking directly to the reader.
    *   The narrator sounds like a kind person. He wants his friends to see the pasture and the leaves and the cows. These lines give the poem a mood of friendship.
    *   The mood is one of sharing and talking. The narrator wants some company as he goes about his business.

        **Content Standard(s): 2**
        **Process Standard(s): 3.5**

### *A Time to Talk* (page 196)

1.  Example of a top score-point response:

    1.  The narrator is a farmer who is working with a hoe.
    2.  The neighbor is riding by on a horse.

    Other possible responses:

    *   Nearby, there are hills used for farming.
    *   Farming, stone walls, and horses are things usually found in a rural area.

        **Content Standard(s): 2**
        **Process Standard(s): 3.5**

2.  Examples of top score-point responses:

    *   Both narrators are very friendly. The narrator of "The Pasture" invites the reader to come along with him as he goes to do chores in a field. The narrator of "A Time to Talk" stops doing his chores in order to talk to a friend. Both narrators value friendship.
    *   Both narrators live in rural areas. Both seem to make their living by working the land. The narrator of "The Pasture" probably raises cattle; he has a mother cow and a baby calf. He also will clear leaves out of a pasture. The narrator of "A Time to Talk" is also probably a farmer; he is outside hoeing fields and hills.

        **Content Standard(s): 2**
        **Process Standard(s): 1.6**

## The World Is Not a Pleasant Place to Be (page 201)

1.  Example of top score-point response:

    - The narrator is saying that life is much more fun when you share it with somebody. It could be a parent, a sibling, or a lover, but everybody needs somebody to be a companion. The narrator uses examples from nature, like clouds and streams, to show that everybody needs somebody.

    **Content Standard(s): 2**
    **Process Standard(s): 3.5**

2.  Examples of top score-point responses:

    | Aspect of Nature | Human Quality or Activity |
    | --- | --- |
    | **A river** | **can decide to stop flowing** |
    | 1. An ocean | sometimes laughs |
    | 2. Clouds | sometimes kiss the ocean |

    Other possible responses:

    - An ocean can cry tears.
    - Clouds and the ocean communicate with each other, sometimes kissing or crying.

    **Content Standard(s): 2**
    **Process Standard(s): 3.5**

## To You (page 201)

1.  Examples of top score-point responses:

    - The narrator is on a quest for knowledge. He wants "to sit and read" and "to sit and learn." This narrator wants to know about the world so that he can make it a better place.

    - The narrator is a dreamer who wants to "make our world anew." The narrator calls out to other dreamers. He wants them to join his effort to make everything better. The narrator feels that knowledge and imagination are tools for improving our planet.

    **Content Standard(s): 2**
    **Process Standard(s): 3.5**

2.  Examples of top score-point responses:

    - The narrator would like to meet dreamers, like himself. He asks for help from "all you who are dreamers, too."

    - The narrator wants to meet people who are like him. He wants to meet people who like to read, learn, use their imaginations, dream, and try to make the world better.

    **Content Standard(s): 2**
    **Process Standard(s): 3.5**

## *What Do Fish Have to Do with Anything?* (page 206)

1. Examples of top score-point responses:

   - Willie's mother is a very careful parent. She believes in following rules and doing things a certain way. She is giving him the recommended amount for one portion, or serving, of cake. She wants to give him the exact amount that is specified on the label.

   - She does not want him to eat too many sweets. She wants to give him the amount that meets the "health requirements." She is probably concerned that her son's diet be very healthy and be very balanced.

   **Content Standard(s): 2**
   **Process Standard(s): 3.5**

2. Examples of top score-point responses:

   - Willie's mother is very concerned about her son. Now that her husband has left, her son has to stay at home by himself at nights. This worries her. Before she leaves for her night-shift job, she asks Willie to recite some important phone numbers. She wants to make sure that Willie knows whom to call if he needs help with something.

   - Willie's mother cannot be with him all the time. She gave him the phone numbers of a neighbor (Mrs. Murphy), his grandmother, her workplace, and the police. Willie's mother wants him to have all these numbers in case he has a problem or an emergency.

   **Content Standard(s): 2**
   **Process Standard(s): 3.5**

3. Examples of top score-point responses:

   - Willie enjoyed talking to the beggar. Perhaps, since his father has left, Willie misses talking to an adult male. The beggar tells him that "Willie" is a boy's name, but that "William" is a grown-up name. The child wants to view himself as a man, not as a boy.

   - Willie feels like his mother is treating him too much like a baby. In an act of rebellion, he shows her that he wants to be treated differently. The name William sounds much more mature than the name Willie.

   **Content Standard(s): 2**
   **Process Standard(s): 3.5**

4. Examples of top score-point responses:

   - Willie is a very curious boy. He cannot help but stare at the beggar. He has a very active mind, and he wants to know the answers to many questions. Willie is not satisfied with simple explanations. He always wants to know why something is true.

   - Willie asks a lot of questions. He asks questions of his mother, his teacher, and the beggar he meets on the street. Willie is always hungry for knowledge and information. He's always trying to figure things out, and he does this by asking a lot of questions. He is not shy at all. He is very curious.

   **Content Standard(s): 2**
   **Process Standard(s): 3.5**

### from *Immigrant Kids* (page 223)

1. Examples of top score-point responses:

   • Most of them came from poor villages in southern and eastern Europe. They crossed the Atlantic Ocean as steerage passengers aboard boats. They paid a low fare so that they could ride in the hold of a ship.

   • They traveled by boat across the Atlantic. Then they had to pass through Ellis Island, which became the nation's chief immigrant processing center in 1892.

   **Content Standard(s): 3**
   **Process Standard(s): 3.5**

2. Examples of top score-point responses:

   • The doctors for the United States Health Service wanted to help people who had trachoma, which can cause blindness. Also, the doctors wanted to confine the movements of people who were suffering from contagious and infectious diseases.

   • Doctors at Ellis Island wanted to reduce the chance that dangerous, infectious diseases were entering the United States. The doctors examined people to try to keep a wave of disease outbreaks from being caused by all the new people who had traveled from Europe and other countries.

   **Content Standard(s): 3**
   **Process Standard(s): 3.5**

3. Examples of top score-point responses:

   • Ellis Island served as a "filter" to keep certain people from entering the United States. Officials certainly wanted to know whether any dangerous, violent criminals were coming into the country. Perhaps the officials hoped to capture immigrants who were running from the law in their native Europe.

   • Millions of people were allowed to pass through Ellis Island. Some people, however, were not allowed into the United States. Perhaps this question was asked in order to "screen" people and keep certain criminals from entering. Also, many of these people had no official records with them, so officials tried to establish a new, permanent set of records for these immigrants.

   **Content Standard(s): 3**
   **Process Standard(s): 3.5**

### *A Christmas Carol* (page 250)

1. Examples of top score-point responses:

   • It is the Christmas season, and Scrooge's hired helpers hope that he will give them a "Christmas bonus" in the form of a coin.

   • Sparsit hopes that Scrooge will be generous and give him a tip, or a Christmas coin. Many employers give their employees some type of Christmas bonus. This gesture angers Scrooge because he is miserly and does not believe in a spirit of generosity for the holiday season.

   **Content Standard(s): 2**
   **Process Standard(s): 3.5**

2.     Examples of top score-point responses:

- As a boy, Scrooge read Robinson Crusoe and Arabian Nights. These were works of fiction.

- Child Scrooge liked to read stories that he would later describe as "fancy." This means illusion. Scrooge liked fantasy books, such as Robinson Crusoe and Arabian Nights. He enjoyed stories that stir the imagination with tales of faraway lands.

   **Content Standard(s): 2**
   **Process Standard(s): 3.5**

3.     Examples of top score-point responses:

- The Second Spirit shows Scrooge that he has been cruel toward others. He is teaching Scrooge a lesson by showing him how he has been selfish. Scrooge's words come back to "haunt" him because he doesn't seem to agree with them now.

- The Second Spirit hopes to show Scrooge how insensitive he has been toward the suffering of others. When Scrooge asks about the health of Tiny Tim, the Second Spirit reminds Scrooge of his comment about the surplus population. Scrooge thought it was okay for some people to just die. When Scrooge asks about shelter for the beggar children, the Second Spirit reminds him of another harsh comment: "Are there no prisons? Are there no workhouses?"

   **Content Standard(s): 2**
   **Process Standard(s): 3.5**

4.     Examples of top score-point responses:

- After the visitation from the spirits, Scrooge experiences a change of heart. He decides to live his life differently. He wants to become a new man. He has learned his lesson, and he now wants to be more kind toward others. Scrooge is happy that Christmas has not passed him by, because he now feels generous.

- Scrooge has decided to change his ways. He decides to be generous. He wakes up with new feelings of generosity. This is really the climax of the play. The first thing he does when he wakes up is to buy a turkey for the Cratchit family. He also visits his nephew, Fred, and he gives the Gentleman Visitor a purse of money to help the needy.

   **Content Standard(s): 2**
   **Process Standard(s): 3.5**

5.     Examples of top score-point responses:

- The theme is to love your neighbor. A stingy old man sees how cruel he has been, and he decides to become a nicer person. The idea is that we should all be considerate of our neighbors, and we should help those who are less fortunate.

- The theme is that people should not ignore the suffering of others. All people, both rich and poor, deserve to be treated with dignity and respect. It is never too late to make a difference in someone's life, and it is never too late to make a difference in your own life. Even the meanest man can change his ways.

   **Content Standard(s): 2**
   **Process Standard(s): 3.5**

### *The Scholarship Jacket* (page 278)

1.   Example of top score-point response:

  • Mr. Boone's reasons for choosing Joann were not fair. He wanted to give the jacket to Joann because her father was an important businessman. Martha, however, deserved the jacket because she is the student who got the highest grades for eight years. Martha is the true class valedictorian.

  **Content Standard(s): 2**
  **Process Standard(s): 1.6, 3.5**

2.   Example of a top score-point response:

  1.   physical education, or P.E.
  2.   history
  3.   math

  **Content Standard(s): 2**
  **Process Standard(s): 3.5**

3.   Example(s):

| Martha's Many Personality Traits |
| --- |
| Excellent student |
| Emotional person |
| Obedient, follows rules |
| Strong sense of justice and fairness |
| Concerned about her physical appearance |
| Determined and brave |

  • Graphic organizers can describe many aspects of Martha's personality. Martha is intelligent, studious, spirited, courageous, self-conscious, and sensitive.

  **Content Standard(s): 2, 4**
  **Process Standard(s): 1.8, 3.5**

### *The Noble Experiment* from *I Never Had it Made* (page 287)

1.   Example of a top score-point response:

  1.   Other players would taunt him and call him hurtful names.
  2.   Pitchers would throw the ball at his head on purpose.

  Other possible responses:

  • Fans would be hostile toward him.
  • Sportswriters would be very critical of him.
  • Robinson would have to "turn the other cheek" and not fight back.

  **Content Standard(s): 3**
  **Process Standard(s): 3.5**

2.    Example of top score-point response:

- Wendell Smith was the sports editor of the black weekly *Pittsburgh Courier*. Smith recommended Jackie Robinson for a tryout with the Boston Red Sox. That team wasn't genuinely interested in hiring a black player. Branch Rickey asked Smith whether any of those players who tried out were "major league material." Smith told him that Robinson was, and that recommendation was partly responsible for Robinson eventually becoming part of the Dodgers team.

    **Content Standard(s): 3**
    **Process Standard(s): 3.5**

3.    Examples of top score-point responses:

- Branch Rickey wanted to make sure that Jackie Robinson knew exactly what kind of abuse he would face. He wanted to "test" Robinson, to see if he could endure this type of hardship. Rickey wanted Robinson to see how people would try to goad him into fighting back or acting in an unsportsmanlike way.

- Not only did Branch Rickey want Jackie Robinson to understand how cruel people would be, he also wanted to test him. If Robinson had not been able to tolerate the name-calling in a quiet office, then there would have been no way that he could have tolerated it on the baseball field.

    **Content Standard(s): 3**
    **Process Standard(s): 3.5**

4.    Examples of top score-point responses:

- Jackie Robinson was a fierce competitor. He welcomed the challenge. He was also very concerned about racial discrimination. He accepted the challenge so that he could help fight against discrimination in major league baseball.

- Jackie Robinson said that he had to do it for many reasons: "For black youth, for my mother, for Rae, for myself." He also said that he felt like he had to do it for Branch Rickey. Jackie Robinson saw an opportunity to become a historical figure. He accepted the challenge. He didn't want to let anyone down. He refused to be scared or to back down. Robinson knew that if he succeeded, then it would be a victory for all African Americans. Jackie Robinson is a great hero.

    **Content Standard(s): 3**
    **Process Standard(s): 3.5**

### *Casey at the Bat* (page 299)

1.    Example of top score-point response:

- Poetry is a form of literature that uses creative language. The poem would have been boring if the poet had always called the baseball "the ball." Using terms like "leather-covered sphere" and "spheroid" adds colorful language to the poem, and these terms help the reader to envision what is happening. These terms also add to the poem's mood of excitement and tension.

    **Content Standard(s): 2**
    **Process Standard(s): 3.5**

2. Examples of top score-point responses:

- Even though he fails in this situation, Casey is considered a good player. The crowd feels that if Casey gets a chance, then the Mudville team will win.

- The crowd thinks that Casey is a good player. The poet reinforces this idea by calling him "mighty Casey." The crowd cheers for Casey. Casey can control the crowd with his gestures; he is probably well respected because he is considered a good player.

   **Content Standard(s): 2**
   **Process Standard(s): 3.5**

3. Examples of top score-point responses:

- The entire poem builds to the climactic moment in which Casey swings the bat with two strikes and two runners on base. Because Casey is portrayed as a hero, the reader expects him to win the game. The ironic thing is that Casey strikes out. Today, he is not the conquering hero.

- The reader expects Casey to save the day. Instead, he strikes out. The poet leads the reader to believe that Casey will win the game for his team. The reader thinks that Casey hit the ball when the poet writes that "the air is shattered by the force of Casey's blow." The last stanza talks about celebration, but only in the final three words of the last line does the reader realize that Casey "has struck out."

   **Content Standard(s): 2**
   **Process Standard(s): 3.5**

4. Example(s):

- Student diagrams should include a depiction of Casey and the crowd, as well as appropriate labels.

   **Content Standard(s): 2, 4**
   **Process Standard(s): 2.1**

### Fable: Ant and Grasshopper (page 312)

1. Examples of top score-point responses:

- Ant worked hard to get her food. Grasshopper did not work at all. Ant thinks, "Why should I help Grasshopper, who didn't do any work at all?" Ant resents the fact that Grasshopper now thinks he can get food from her.

- Ant says to Grasshopper, "I worked hard all through the summer, storing food for the winter." Ant feels that all her hard work has now paid off. Ant thinks that those who work deserve to benefit from their work, and that those who goof off deserve to suffer later.

   **Content Standard(s): 2**
   **Process Standard(s): 3.5**

2.     Examples of top score-point responses:

- This moral is similar to another lesson: "Failing to prepare is preparing to fail." If you study hard the night before a test, you will probably do well. If you decide to play a game or watch TV instead of studying, then you will probably do poorly. The ant would probably study and then do well on the test. The grasshopper would probably waste his time and then do poorly on the test.

- If you have a job and you save your money, then you have something to fall back on. Suppose that you had to quit your job, or your job got eliminated. That would be a case of "bad times." If you had saved your money during the "good times," then you would have something to rely on while you tried to get a new job. The grasshopper wasted his time, so he had no food in the winter. If you waste your money, then you won't have anything during an emergency, when you really need it.

**Content Standard(s): 2**
**Process Standard(s): 3.5**

### *Poetry: The Ant and the Grasshopper* (page 312)

1.     Example of a top score-point response:

1.   "Green as a lime" compares the color of the grasshopper to the color of a lime.
2.   "Sharp as a splinter" compares the ant's glance to the sharpness of a splinter.

Other possible responses:

- "As cold as lime ice" compares the coldness of the grasshopper's body to the coldness of ice.

**Content Standard(s): 2**
**Process Standard(s): 3.5**

2.     Examples of top score-point responses:

- The moral is "Hard work isn't easy to beat." This means that there is a reward for working hard. The ant worked hard during the summer, so she has plenty to eat in the winter. The grasshopper, who did not work hard, has no food to eat.

- Those who work hard enjoy the fruits of their labor. Those who are lazy will struggle and regret their laziness. The grasshopper is stiff and lame because she is stuck outside in the winter. The grasshopper has no home, and she has no food because she didn't do any work.

**Content Standard(s): 2**
**Process Standard(s): 3.5**

3.    Example(s):

| Differences Between the Fable and the Poem |
| --- |
| 1. One is written as prose, but the other is written as poetry. |
| 2. In the fable, the grasshopper is male and the ant is female. In the poem, both characters are female. |
| 3. In the poem, the grasshopper insults the ant in the summer. This does not happen in the fable. |
| 4. In the fable, the ant speaks to the grasshopper. In the poem, the ant does not speak. |

| Similarities Between the Fable and the Poem |
| --- |
| 1. In both passages, the grasshopper is left out in the cold without food. |
| 2. In both passages, the ant has a home, but the grasshopper does not. |
| 3. In both passages, the ant works hard, but the grasshopper does not. |

Content Standard(s): 2, 4
Process Standard(s): 1.6, 1.8

### The Richer, the Poorer (page 316)

1.    Examples of top score-point responses:

- Lottie grew up during a time when there were few job opportunities for women, especially African-American women. Lottie did not want to "give up a job that paid well for a homemaking job that paid nothing." For Lottie, getting married meant giving up her profession, and she did not want to do that. She feared taking this risk.

- Lottie was almost persuaded to marry a few times, but she wanted to focus on her career. She thought it was more important to stick with a stable job than to risk her future by getting married.

Content Standard(s): 2
Process Standard(s): 3.5

2.    Example of top score-point response:

|            | Bess | | Lottie | |
| --- | --- | --- | --- | --- |
| | **married Harry** | | **remained single** | |
| | 1. as a child, did not work | | 1. as a child, worked as a clerk | |
| | 2. had lots of adventures | | 2. lived a routine life | |

Content Standard(s): 2
Process Standard(s): 1.6, 1.8

3.    Examples of top score-point responses:

- Focusing too much on money/financial issues can lead to sadness. Living life to the fullest is the most important thing to do. Lottie was able to save money, but it didn't truly give her happiness because her life was too dull.

- Bess didn't seem to save any money. Lottie seemed too focused on saving money. Perhaps the secret to happiness is finding the right balance. You shouldn't focus on money all the time, but you shouldn't foolishly waste your money, either. If Bess hadn't had a sister to help her, she would have remained stranded. In the end, Lottie decided to "kick up her heels" and live her life more fully. It's never too late to change.

Content Standard(s): 2
Process Standard(s): 3.5

### *One Ordinary Day, with Peanuts* (page 348)

1. Example of top score-point response:

   - Mr. Johnson spent his day being helpful and generous toward others. He filled his pockets with peanuts so that he could give them away throughout his day. He gave some peanuts to the boy who was moving to Vermont. He met one man who wanted a dime; Mr. Johnson gave him a peanut with a dollar wrapped around it. He also fed peanuts to the pigeons.

     **Content Standard(s): 2**
     **Process Standard(s): 3.5**

2. Examples of top score-point responses:

   - Mr. Johnson wanted to find just the right man. The man had to be in a hurry because he was late for work. He had to be a good match for Mildred Kent, or at least look like he would be a good match. The author describes Mr. Johnson, during the selection process, "as one who must make a choice involving perhaps whole years of lives."

   - Mr. Johnson had to find the right man because he was "playing matchmaker." He was trying to find the right person to spend the day with Miss Kent. Mr. Johnson was observing people, perhaps looking at men's hands to find a fellow who was not wearing a wedding band.

     **Content Standard(s): 2**
     **Process Standard(s): 3.5**

3. Examples of top score-point responses:

   | Name or Description of Character | Mr. Johnson's Action(s) |
   |---|---|
   | **Arthur Adams** | **Mr. Johnson introduced Arthur Adams to Mildred Kent and gave the couple some money.** |
   | 1. Taxi cab driver | Mr. Johnson gave him advice on race horse betting. |
   | 2. Woman moving to Vermont | Mr. Johnson watched her son for her while the moving van was there. |
   | 3. Bus driver | Mr. Johnson gave him a peanut. |
   | Other possibilities:<br>• Couple searching for apartment<br>• Boy in a carriage<br>• Mrs. Johnson | Other possibilities:<br>• gave them address of vacant apartment<br>• gave him a carnation<br>• told her of his daily adventures |

   **Content Standard(s): 2**
   **Process Standard(s): 3.5**

4. Examples of top score-point responses:

- Tomorrow, Mr. Johnson will become the mean person and Mrs. Johnson will become the nice person. They will trade roles. He will spend his day doing cruel acts, and she will spend her day doing kind acts. The surprise ending to this story reveals that the two characters "switch places" on alternating days.

- The surprising thing is that Mr. Johnson will spend his next day being mean. Throughout the story, you wonder, "Why is he being so nice to everyone?" The answer to that question is never really given; however, we do know that Mr. Johnson will "trade places" with his wife tomorrow, and he will do random acts of cruelty instead of random acts of kindness. This story is unusual because Mr. and Mrs. Johnson do not seem to have any kind of normal jobs.

**Content Standard(s): 2**
**Process Standard(s): 3.5**

### *Amigo Brothers* (page 361)

1. Examples of top score-point responses:

Spanish (or Spanish American) Words      English Language Translation

| suavecito | Take it easy. |
|---|---|
| 1. Sabe? | You know? |
| 2. panin | buddy |
| 3. cheverote | really cool |
| Other possibilities:<br>• amigo<br>• hermano<br>• Loisaida<br>• mucho corazón | Other possibilities:<br>• friend<br>• brother<br>• Lower East Side<br>• a lot of heart |

**Content Standard(s): 2**
**Process Standard(s): 3.5**

2. Examples of top score-point responses:

- Felix went to the movies to try to take his mind off of his upcoming fight against Antonio. His plan did not work. It had the opposite effect. As Felix watched the film, he kept imagining that he was the character in the movie, and that he was fighting Antonio.

- Felix imagined himself as The Champion, and he pictured Antonio as The Challenger. Although this was not his initial intention, Felix used the film as a way to "psyche himself up" for his boxing match against his good friend Antonio.

**Content Standard(s): 2**
**Process Standard(s): 3.5**

3.     Example of a top score-point response:

1.  They fight in the same weight class: Lightweight.
2.  They both have a Puerto Rican heritage.
3.  They grew up in the same Manhattan tenement building.

Other possible responses:

- They both want to win the fight and maintain their friendship.
- They work out together.
- They both collect boxing magazines.
- They wear similar clothing when they exercise (sweatshirts, handkerchiefs).
  **Content Standard(s): 2**
  **Process Standard(s): 1.6**

4.     Example of top score-point response:

- Each fighter knocked his opponent down in the second round of the fight. Neither fighter scored a knockout. It is difficult to determine who won, but Antonio might have won because he had a height advantage. He was taller. He was considered the better boxer. The author writes, "Neither gave an inch," so it is hard to say who won, but it seems like Antonio did.

- Felix may have won the fight. He knocked Antonio down and clearly injured him. Blood was pouring from Antonio's nose. Felix had a puffy eye, but it seems like he got the best of his friend/opponent Antonio.

  **Content Standard(s): 2**
  **Process Standard(s): 3.5**

## *Ode to an Artichoke* (page 375)

1.     Example of top score-point response:

- The poet compares the artichoke to an armored warrior. The plant's scales are its "armor." The plant is "equipped like a soldier" and has a "martial" existence. The plant dies in a cooking pot, similar to the way that a soldier dies in battle.

  **Content Standard(s): 2**
  **Process Standard(s): 3.5**

2.     Example(s):

| The Life of an Artichoke: Key Events |
| --- |
| 1. It grows in a kitchen garden. |
| 2. It gets carried away in a big willow basket. |
| 3. It arrives at the fair. |
| 4. It gets purchased and dumped in Maria's bag. |
| 5. It gets drowned in a cooking pot. |
| 6. It is served on a plate and eaten by people. |

   **Content Standard(s): 2, 4**
   **Process Standard(s): 1.8**

3.    Example of top score-point response:

- The poet writes that the cabbage is "trying on skirts." This phrase describes all the layers of leaves on a head of cabbage. The poet is comparing the layers of the plant to layers of clothing. This is appropriate because a head of cabbage has many layers.

    **Content Standard(s): 2**
    **Process Standard(s): 3.5**

### from *An American Childhood* (page 381)

1.    Example(s):

- Student diagrams should include the three characters and the four elements listed above. The diagrams should also be labeled.

    **Content Standard(s): 3, 4**
    **Process Standard(s): 2.1**

2.    Example of a top score-point response:

1.  The author compares the chase to running all the way to Panama. She actually only ran about ten blocks in a Pittsburgh neighborhood.

2.  The author says that the driver could have boiled her in oil. In actuality, all the driver did was to give the kids a lecture.

    Other possible responses:

- The author mentions forms of punishment that the driver could use, such as "dismembered us piecemeal," "staked us to anthills," and "cut off our heads."

    **Content Standard(s): 3**
    **Process Standard(s): 3.5**

3.    Example of top score-point response:

- An iceball was generally not to be thrown at a person, although that did occasionally happen. An iceball was "perfectly spherical, and squeezed perfectly translucent so no snow remained all the way through." An iceball was made from "perfectly white snow." A typical snowball, however, was made for throwing and could be made from any type of snow.

    **Content Standard(s): 3**
    **Process Standard(s): 1.6**

4.    Examples of top score-point responses:

- The narrator seemed to enjoy getting in trouble, and she enjoyed throwing snowballs. Not only did the lecture not stop her, it probably actually encouraged her to keep on throwing snowballs at cars.

- The lecture probably did not change the narrator's behavior. The narrator seemed thrilled and exhilarated to be chased by an adult. The author admits to being "terrified," but her response to the lecture suggests that it had little effect on her. Early in the passage, the author writes, "I got in trouble throwing snowballs and have seldom been happier since." This indicates that the narrator was not particularly upset about being "chewed out" by the driver.

    **Content Standard(s): 3**
    **Process Standard(s): 3.5**

### The Bat (page 391)

1. Examples of top score-point responses:

   • The poet compares the bat to a mouse because it stays hidden (from human sight) all day long, similar to a mouse. The poet calls the bat a "cousin to the mouse," and he refers to bats as "mice with wings." Bats are like mice because they are quiet and they live in the attic. With their small size and furry bodies, they also resemble mice.

   • The poet also compares the bat to a human. The poet writes that bats "can wear a human face." This description compares a bat's facial expressions to those of a person because the expressions can be so dramatic.

   **Content Standard(s): 2**
   **Process Standard(s): 3.5**

2. Example of top score-point response:

   • The last word in each line of a stanza rhymes in this poem ("house" and "mouse," "head" and "dead"). The poem is made up of five rhyming couplets.

   **Content Standard(s): 2**
   **Process Standard(s): 1.6**

### Mooses (page 391)

1. Examples of top score-point responses:

   • The narrator thinks that the moose is not very intelligent. He describes them as "goofy" and calls them "dopes." The narrator portrays the moose as an oversized, confused, slow-witted animal.

   • He thinks the moose is so dumb that it cannot even tell the difference between a mirror and another moose. The narrator has a very low opinion of this animal.

   **Content Standard(s): 2**
   **Process Standard(s): 3.5**

2. Examples of top score-point responses:

   | Animal | Human Behavior or Trait |
   |--------|------------------------|
   | **Bat** | **has facial expressions like a human's** |
   | 1. Bat | has "fingers" that make a "hat" |
   | 2. Moose | has emotions; weeps |
   | 3. Moose | is self-conscious about its appearance |

   **Content Standard(s): 2**
   **Process Standard(s): 1.6**

### The Monsters Are Due on Maple Street (page 415)

1. Example of top score-point response:

   • These stage directions indicate camera movements, such as "The camera moves over to a shot of the ice cream vendor...." Another stage direction is "The camera takes us across the porches again." These directions help the director to decide how to film the drama. On the written page, these directions make the action more vivid for the reader.

   **Content Standard(s): 2**
   **Process Standard(s): 1.6**

2. Examples of top score-point responses:

   • Charlie didn't really mean to kill Pete Van Horn. He just kind of "lost his head" and in the heat of the moment, he shot Pete because he thought he was a monster.

   • Charlie became frightened and paranoid. This caused him to act in an irrational way. After the power goes out, the crowd begins to think that monsters have invaded their neighborhood. (This shows the power of suggestion.) Charlie shot Pete Van Horn because he mistakenly thought that he was an alien invader.

   **Content Standard(s): 2**
   **Process Standard(s): 3.5**

3. Examples of top score-point responses:

   • The crowd has worked itself into a frenzy. Almost everyone has become paranoid. The perfectly normal hobbies of star-gazing and radio-making suddenly seem suspect because the crowd is looking for a scapegoat.

   • The crowd thinks that Les is staring at the stars because he is an alien, or he is at least communicating with aliens. Similarly, they think Steve uses his radio to communicate with aliens. In a sarcastic attempt to show how silly the implied accusation is, Steve says, "I talk to monsters from outer space." The crowd thinks that aliens have turned off the power.

   **Content Standard(s): 2**
   **Process Standard(s): 3.5**

4. Examples of top score-point responses:

   • At the play's conclusion, the narrator says, "Prejudices can kill and suspicion can destroy." The theme of this drama is that difficult situations can cause human prejudices to come out. There is a great danger when humans lose their ability for rational, logical thinking. People can easily be manipulated into doing dangerous and cruel things.

   • Modern humans are so dependent on technology that they seem to lose their minds without it. When the people are unable to use their cars, radios, lights, and telephones, they become paranoid and turn against one another.

   **Content Standard(s): 2**
   **Process Standard(s): 3.5**

5. Example of top score-point response:

- As revealed in Act Two, Scene Two, the characters in the spacecraft caused the power failure on Maple Street. These characters are only identified as Figure One and Figure Two. They are space aliens who have figured out how to turn a peaceful group of people into a ruthless mob. The aliens do this simply by manipulating human technology. They knock out all the electricity and telephones. They cause an automobile to start and stop. These unexpected events cause the neighbors to grow very suspicious of one another.

   **Content Standard(s): 2**
   **Process Standard(s): 3.5**

### Key Item (page 432)

1. Example of a top score-point response:

   1. weather
   2. politics
   3. economics

   Other possible responses:

   - farm unrest
   - jetstream flow

      **Content Standard(s): 2**
      **Process Standard(s): 3.5**

2. Example(s):

   | Differences Between the Passages |
   | --- |
   | 1. In one, the villain is a supercomputer, and in the other, it is a space alien. |
   | 2. One is set in the current day (or perhaps the past), and the other is set in the future. |
   | 3. One is a teleplay, and the other is a short story. |

   | Similarities Between the Passages |
   | --- |
   | 1. Both passages have characters that are extremely dependent upon machines. |
   | 2. Both passages have characters that are starting to "crack" under pressure. |
   | 3. Both passages are from the science fiction genre. |

   **Content Standard(s): 2, 4**
   **Process Standard(s): 1.6, 1.8**

3. Example of top score-point response:

   - Weaver said, "Please!" Apparently, Multivac has become so advanced that it now has human feelings. It would not function properly until it was treated politely. The machine was simply being stubborn. Multivac now has feelings, so it is no longer just a machine. It is something more than that.

      **Content Standard(s): 2**
      **Process Standard(s): 3.5**

### *The Serial Garden* (page 438)

1.  Example of top score-point response:

    - Mark placed this ad because he wants to reunite Mr. Johansen with the princess. Mark's mother threw out his magical Brekkfast Brikks garden. In order to construct a new one, Mark must find more packets of the cereal. That is why he has placed the classified advertisement.

    **Content Standard(s): 2**
    **Process Standard(s): 3.5**

2.  Examples of top score-point responses:

    - The author gives the cereal a funny name that sounds like "bricks." Also, the characters make funny comments about how bad the cereal tastes. Mark adds a lot of ingredients (milk and sugar) when eating the cereal because it tastes so bad.

    - The cereal doesn't taste very good, and the author uses humor when describing it. Mark says the Brekkfast Brikks taste like "tiny doormats." His father says they "taste just like esparto grass." Later, Mr. Armitage said that "he wouldn't taste another Brekkfast Brikk even if it were wrapped in an inch-thick layer of *pâté de foie gras*." These descriptions all use exaggeration to describe the foul taste of the cereal.

    **Content Standard(s): 2**
    **Process Standard(s): 3.5**

3.  Example of top score-point response:

    - The larder mouse nibbled on the corner of the cereal packet that contained Section Six. When Mark went back to the garden, the grotto had a hole in it. The princess feared the intruder, a "wild beast" with "tracks like those of a big bear." It was just a little mouse, but from the princess's perspective, that is a large beast.

    **Content Standard(s): 2**
    **Process Standard(s): 3.5**

4.  Example(s):

    - Student diagrams should include elements from the story, such as flowers, cabbages, the grotto, or the yew arch. The diagrams should also be labeled.

    **Content Standard(s): 2, 4**
    **Process Standard(s): 2.1**

### *Jabberwocky* (page 458)

1.  Example of top score-point response:

    - A boy goes to the Tumtum tree. There, he uses a sword to slay a monster called the Jabberwock. His father is very proud of the boy.

    **Content Standard(s): 2**
    **Process Standard(s): 3.5**

2. Example of top score-point response:

- The author, Lewis Carroll, uses made-up words, such as "slithy," "tulgey," and "frabjous." The reader can still understand the events in the poem, despite this weird language.

   **Content Standard(s): 2**
   **Process Standard(s): 3.5**

### *Sarah Cynthia Sylvia Stout Would Not Take the Garbage Out* (page 458)

1. Examples of top score-point responses:

- You should always take the garbage out on a regular basis. Sarah refused to do it, and by the time she had changed her mind, it was too late. She had lost all her friends and neighbors. Something awful happened to her. Perhaps the garbage fell on her. This happened because she did not do her chores properly.

- Do not procrastinate. Do not put off until tomorrow the thing that you should do today. The longer that you put off doing an awful task, the worse it will become. There is a price to pay for being lazy.

   **Content Standard(s): 2**
   **Process Standard(s): 3.5**

2. Examples of top score-point responses:

Consonant Sound                                    Phrase

| The "S" Sound | "Sarah Cynthia Sylvia Stout" |
|---|---|
| 1. Repetition of the "P" Sound | "prune pits, peach pits, orange peels" |
| 2. Repetition of the "G" Sound | "globs of gooey bubble gum" |
| 3. Repetition of the "B" Sound | "black burned buttered toast" |

Other possibilities:

- "potato peelings"
- "gloppy glumps"
- "green baloney, Rubbery blubbery macaroni"

   **Content Standard(s): 2**
   **Process Standard(s): 3.5**

3. Examples of top score-point responses:

- Both poems use language in a very creative way. Both poems use rhyme, and both have lines that end with words that rhyme. Both are fun to read aloud because of the poet's emphasis on sound devices.

- Both poems use alliteration, which is the repetition of consonant sounds at the beginnings of words and syllables. In "Jabberwocky," there is rhyme ("boy," "joy") and alliteration ("Callooh! Callay!"). The poem "Sarah Cynthia Sylvia Stout Would Not Take the Garbage Out" also contains rhyme ("Stout," "out") and alliteration ("moldy melons," "french fries").

   **Content Standard(s): 2**
   **Process Standard(s): 1.6**

### *The Eternal Frontier* (page 463)

1.  Examples of top score-point responses:

    *   The author is demonstrating how quickly technology progressed in the twentieth century. He mentions the 144 miles so that he can contrast that with the more than 3,000,000 miles of surfaced road in the U.S.A. today. The author implies that we are just beginning to explore the possibilities of space travel.

    *   For the author, this shows how humans are constantly striving to go greater distances and to explore more areas. At one time, paved roads were a new thing. Now they are common. Similarly, space travel is now a relatively new thing. In the future it will be common. Humans will travel on "roads" that cut through outer space.

        **Content Standard(s): 3**
        **Process Standard(s): 3.5**

2.  Examples of top score-point responses:

    *   The author views outer space as a frontier that must be explored. The essay title "The Eternal Frontier" suggests the limitless possibilities offered by outer space exploration. At the end of the essay, the author describes the benefits to everyday life that are a result of the space program, including computing devices and Teflon.

    *   The author thinks that we should continue to explore outer space. To do otherwise would be to "live in the past." The author compares those who would ignore the opportunities of space exploration to people who are still stuck in a cave (prehistoric man). The author links space exploration with all kinds of positive progress and destiny.

        **Content Standard(s): 3**
        **Process Standard(s): 3.5**

3.  Examples of top score-point responses:

    *   The author argues that it is our "destiny" to explore space. Space travel is dangerous and expensive. People have died in the space program. It costs millions of dollars to put rockets into space, and the benefits are not worth the expense. Tax dollars should go to other programs (defense, education, etc.).

    *   As the author himself notes, we have many problems here on Earth. The author doesn't recognize the importance of protecting our environment. Why should we spend all this time, money, and effort on space exploration when the most important thing we can do is to improve Earth's environment? We should save our planet before we continue exploring other planets.

        **Content Standard(s): 3**
        **Process Standard(s): 2.3**

### *Dark They Were, and Golden-Eyed* (page 478)

1.  Examples of top score-point responses:

    *   This story uses third-person limited point of view. Although the reader experiences the story's events mostly through Mr. Bittering's perspective, the narrator does not use "I" or "me."

    *   This is third-person limited point of view. The narrator refers to the main character as "Harry," not as "I." The narrator tells us what Harry is thinking, but the narrator is also able to observe Harry's behavior.

        **Content Standard(s): 2**
        **Process Standard(s): 3.5**

2.     Examples of top score-point responses:

• These two characters will turn into Martians, just like the Bittering family and all the other colonists from Earth. In this story, people from Earth eventually turn into Martians.

• They will become Martians. Their skin and eyes will change colors. They will begin to speak the Martian language. The environment of the planet causes all of its inhabitants to become Martians, even if they were born on Earth. Martians seem to think and act as a group; they seem to be very similar to each other.

**Content Standard(s): 2**
**Process Standard(s): 3.5**

3.     Examples of top score-point responses:

• The captain is doing the same thing that the earlier Mars colonists did. They used names of places on Earth for features on Mars. Eventually, however, they replaced these names with Martian names. As the people became Martians, they started using more and more Martian language.

• The captain is selecting names that honor great leaders from the United States. These are the types of names with which he is most familiar. There are cities in the United States with similar names: Lincoln, Nebraska, and Washington, D.C. In time, the captain will abandon these names in favor of Martian ones.

**Content Standard(s): 2**
**Process Standard(s): 3.5**

4.     Example(s):

| The Bitterings' Life on Earth | The Bitterings' Life on Mars |
|---|---|
| Cows have two horns. | Cows have three horns. |
| Human eyes are blue, green, gray, or brown. | All human eyes are yellow. |
| They speak English. | They speak Martian. |
| Each person has an individual memory. | They seem to forget about the past and lose interest in things related to Earth. |

**Content Standard(s): 2, 4**
**Process Standard(s): 1.6, 1.8**

5.     Examples of top score-point responses:

• In the early part of the story, Harry was very uncomfortable with life on Mars. He refused to even eat food that was grown on Mars. He yearned to go back to Earth. As time passed, however, Harry turned into a Martian. He stopped yearning for his life back on Earth. Once his transformation occurred, he felt no desire to travel back to Earth.

• On Mars, people slowly become Martians. Their bodies and minds change to become Martian instead of human. Harry resists the transformation, but eventually it happens. He begins to feel more comfortable on Mars. His rocket gathers rust. He abandons it after he and his family go to the villa. The Martians establish a new settlement and leave everything else behind.

**Content Standard(s): 2**
**Process Standard(s): 3.5**

### The Golden Kite, the Silver Wind (page 492)

1.  Examples of top score-point responses:

    *   People should work together instead of constantly competing against one another. When the two towns cooperated instead of competing, both of them prospered.

    *   The leaders of the two towns tried to outdo each other with different types of walls. Once they stopped doing all that non-productive work, the two towns became like a kite carried by the wind. Both parties benefited. This is a story with many symbols. The people in the towns could not pay attention to more important things because they were so busy fixing the walls over and over.

        **Content Standard(s): 2**
        **Process Standard(s): 3.5**

2.  Example of top score-point response:

| The Shape of the First Town's Wall | The Shape of the Kwan-Si Town Wall |
|---|---|
| **Orange** | **Pig** |
| 1. Club | Bonfire |
| 2. Lake | Mouth |
| 3. Needle | Sword |

    **Content Standard(s): 2**
    **Process Standard(s): 3.5**

3.  Example of top score-point response:

    *   The Mandarin's daughter is wiser than her father. She figures out ways to make her town's wall better than the wall of Kwan-Si. She whispers directions from behind the screen. Yet, she is also the character who sees how pointless it is to keep changing the walls. At the end of the story, the daughter comes up with a plan that allows both towns to live in peace and prosperity.

        **Content Standard(s): 2**
        **Process Standard(s): 3.5**

### *The White Umbrella* (page 522)

1.   Examples of top score-point responses:

   • The umbrella was very white, and Mona played the piano very poorly.

   • The author compares the umbrella to a royal baton, and she compares Mona's piano playing to the sound of cats fighting. The author uses a simile to liken the umbrella to a scepter. She uses a metaphor to compare the sour piano notes to the sounds of cats screeching.

   **Content Standard(s): 2**
   **Process Standard(s): 3.5**

2.   Examples of top score-point responses:

   • The narrator wants to keep secret the fact that her mother now has a job. The narrator disapproves of her mother's decision to start working. The narrator is afraid that if she and her sister, Mona, go back inside, then Miss Crosman will eventually discover that their mother now has a job.

   • The narrator's pride prevents her from going back into the house. She doesn't want any sympathy from Miss Crosman. She lies to Miss Crosman in an effort to keep the woman from realizing that her mother has a job that does not match the narrator's expectations. At one point, the author writes, "I knew that I was in store for another bolt of sympathy...." This sentence demonstrates the narrator's disdain for Miss Crosman's sympathy. The narrator doesn't want anyone to feel sorry for her family.

   **Content Standard(s): 2**
   **Process Standard(s): 3.5**

3.   Examples of top score-point responses:

   • This story is about the narrator trying to fit into mainstream American society. She feels a bit alienated because of her Chinese heritage. Early on in the story, the author writes, "The Lees were the only other Chinese family in town." This sentence tells us that the narrator's family was one of only two Chinese families in that city. The narrator probably felt somewhat like an outsider. The white umbrella symbolizes being a part of mainstream society. It could also represent the act of changing so that you fit in better with a society. At the end of the story, when the girl throws the umbrella in the sewer, it is a symbolic act. This act symbolizes her decision to accept her roots, her heritage, and her true self.

   • For the narrator, the white umbrella is a symbol of being a popular, well-liked member of the school's social circles. The narrator says, "I wanted to dangle it from my wrist on the way to school the way the other girls did." The narrator wants to be like Eugenie Roberts. The umbrella, with its bright white color and shining silver handle, also represents status and elegance.

   **Content Standard(s): 2**
   **Process Standard(s): 3.5**

4. Example of top score-point response:

- The mother was afraid that her daughters would become ashamed of her. The mother thought that the girls would not approve of the job she accepted. The narrator tells Miss Crosman that her mother is a concert pianist. This is obviously a lie. The narrator envisions her mother "selling perfume, testing recipes for the local newspaper," or perhaps working for a florist. These jobs are ones that meet the narrator's expectations. When the narrator learns that her mother is working as a grocery store check-out clerk, she is disappointed. She tells her mother, "I wish you would quit." For the narrator, those types of jobs are acceptable for "American people," but not for her mother.

   **Content Standard(s): 2**
   **Process Standard(s): 3.5**

## from Boy: Tales of Childhood (page 533)

1. Examples of top score-point responses:

- The boy's father, who was a doctor, had convinced him that this particular candy was made of rats' bodies. (His father had caught him eating the candy in bed.) His father warned him against the dangers of eating this candy. In reality, the doctor was simply trying to break his son of the habit of eating too many sweets. Eating too much candy can damage your teeth.

- Dr. Thwaites said that all of the nation's rat catchers sold their rats to the Licorice Bootlace Factory. There, the rats were boiled, smashed, and cut into strips. Eating these strips could give you "ratitis." This disease was caused by eating animals that had consumed rat poison. Sufferers of "ratitis" grew tails and sharp teeth. The other boys freely ate the candy, but Thwaites did not. His father's wild story had made an impression upon him.

   **Content Standard(s): 3**
   **Process Standard(s): 3.5**

2. Examples of top score-point responses:

- One example is when the author writes, "My only ambition, my hope, my longing was to have a bike like that and to go whizzing down the hill with no hands on the handlebars." The narrator is exaggerating when describing the excitement he felt. That was not truly his only life ambition, so this is a case of exaggeration used for comic effect. A second example is when the boys became excited about the Mouse Plot. The author writes, "We felt like a gang of desperados setting out to rob a train or blow up the sheriff's office." The narrator is comparing a group of mischievous little boys to a bloodthirsty gang of Old West outlaws.

- Dr. Thwaites's description of how licorice bootlaces were made is a passage that is filled with hyperbole. The disease "ratitis" does not exist. It is a disease that causes you to grow a tail and sharp teeth. This is merely an exaggeration of health problems that could be caused by eating too much candy. The description of Mrs. Pratchett's filthy appearance may also contain a bit of hyperbole. (It's hard to believe that the owner of a candy store would actually be that dirty.) After the boys see the broken candy jar, the author writes, "Alarm bells were beginning to ring faintly in our ears." This is a metaphor. It is also an exaggeration of the way the boys were feeling. They felt a lot of anxiety because of their prank.

   **Content Standard(s): 3**
   **Process Standard(s): 3.5**

3.    Example of top score-point response:

- Mr. Coombes did this in order to help Mrs. Pratchett identify the pranksters who had put the dead mouse in the candy jar. It would have been difficult for Mrs. Pratchett to walk through every classroom and hallway in the school. Therefore, all the children were forced to line up outside. This plan worked. When she saw Thwaites, she yelled, "That's one of 'em! I'd know 'im a mile away, the scummy little bounder!" She identified all the pranksters, and they were punished.

    **Content Standard(s): 3**
    **Process Standard(s): 3.5**

4.    Example(s):

| Key Events and What They Indicate about Roald Dahl's Personality as a Boy |
|---|
| 1. Mischievous: The prank with the dead mouse shows that he was a mischievous boy. |
| 2. Insecure: After he had pulled off the prank, he viewed himself as a popular hero. This shows that he longed for the other boys' acceptance and approval. He wanted to be popular. |
| 3. Sociable: He liked to hang out with a crowd of friends. This shows that he was sociable, gregarious. |
| 4. Adventurous: He longed to be like the older boy who rode a bicycle without putting his hands on the handlebars. This showed his spirit of adventure. |
| 5. Intimidated: The description of Mr. Coombes as a giant shows that Dahl was intimidated by police officers, headmasters, and other authority figures. Since he was mischievous, perhaps he had good reason to fear these authority figures. |

    **Content Standard(s): 3, 4**
    **Process Standard(s): 1.8**

5.    Example of a top score-point response:

1.  Licorice bootlaces
2.  Sherbet suckers
3.  Pear drops
4.  Tonsil ticklers
5.  Gobstoppers

Other possible responses:

- Strawberry bonbons
- Glacier mints
- Bull's-eyes
- Old-fashioned humbugs
- Acid drops
- Lemon drops
- Treacle toffee
- Wine gums
- Nut clusters
- Chocolate fudge

    **Content Standard(s): 3**
    **Process Standard(s): 3.5**

### *A Defenseless Creature* (page 553)

1.    Examples of top score-point responses:

- People use the expression "pull my hair out" to describe how they feel during an extremely stressful situation. In this play, two characters (Mrs. Schukin and Mr. Kistunov) literally pull their hair out. In one comic episode, Mrs. Schukin puts a clump of her hair on Mr. Kistunov's desk. In another episode, she jumps up on his desk and kicks his desk bell. This is also a funny example of something that probably would not happen in real life.

- Mrs. Schukin annoys Mr. Kistunov so much that he decides to actually give her the money. This is a comedic and unrealistic plot device. In real life, a bank official would not give someone money just because that person was being very annoying. Also, Mr. Kistunov commands his employee to strike/beat Mrs. Schukin. Nowadays, that command would never be made. In this play, it is an exaggeration, intended for comic effect.

     **Content Standard(s): 2**
     **Process Standard(s): 3.5**

2.    Example of top score-point response:

- Mrs. Schukin wants Mr. Kistunov to give her 24 rubles and 36 kopecks. (Eventually, he does decide to give her the money so that she will leave him alone.) Her husband has lost his job. His employer deducted 24 rubles and 36 kopecks from his pay because he had borrowed money from the employees' fund. Mrs. Schukin thinks that this deduction was an error. She demands that the bank give her this much money, even though this dispute actually has nothing to do with the bank.

     **Content Standard(s): 2**
     **Process Standard(s): 3.5**

3.    Example of top score-point response:

- The scene takes place in a bank office, so the stage will need a room with a door. Also required are a desk, two chairs, and perhaps a name plate for Mr. Kistunov's desk. He will also need a crutch and perhaps a footstool because of his injury. His desk must have a desk bell for Mrs. Schukin to ring. His office should be filled with the typical items found in a bank official's office, such as ink, pens, papers, books, folders, filing cabinets, etc. One key prop is the doctor's certificate that Mrs. Schukin presents. A piece of parchment, a scroll, or any official-looking paper can serve as this certificate.

     **Content Standard(s): 2**
     **Process Standard(s): 3.5**

### *The Highwayman* (page 564)

1.    Examples of top score-point responses:

- With redcoat soldiers guarding her, this bound woman shot herself. She did this in order to warn The Highwayman of the treacherous soldiers.

- Bess waited for her highwayman. Meanwhile, some soldiers came and tied her up. She got her hand free and shot herself. The soldiers also shot the highwayman.

     **Content Standard(s): 2**
     **Process Standard(s): 3.5**

2.      Example of top score-point response:

•       The highwayman rides a horse, so this poem takes place before the invention of cars. The streets are made of cobblestone, so this was before roads were paved. King George's men are present, and they are called "a redcoat troop." They carry muskets, and the highwayman wears doeskin breeches. All of these details suggest the Revolutionary War era, or the period just before that, in the 1700s.

        **Content Standard(s): 2**
        **Process Standard(s): 3.5**

3.      Examples of top score-point responses:

        Consonant Sound                                    Phrase

| **Repetition of the "G" Sound** | **"a ghostly galleon"** |
|---|---|
| 1. Repetition of the "C" Sound | "over the cobbles he clattered and clashed" |
| 2. Repetition of the "D" Sound | "Down like a dog on the highway" |
| 3. Repetition of the "L" Sound | "But he loved the landlord's daughter,/ The landlord's red-lipped daughter" |

Other possibilities:

•       "the black cascade of perfume came tumbling over"
•       "Dumb as a dog he listened"
•       "jeweled twinkle, His pistol butts a-twinkle. His rapier hilt a-twinkle, under the jeweled"
        **Content Standard(s): 2**
        **Process Standard(s): 3.5**

## *An Hour with Abuelo* (page 591)

1.      Examples of top score-point responses:

        Spanish Word or Phrase                             English Language Translation

| **abuelo** | **grandfather** |
|---|---|
| 1. una hora | one hour |
| 2. Gracias, hijo. | Thank you, son. |
| 3. sí | yes |
| Other possibilities:<br>• Ay, bendito!<br>• Así es la vida.<br>• campo<br>• guayabera<br>• *POEMAS DE ARTURO* | Other possibilities:<br>• Oh, goodness!<br>• That's the way life is.<br>• countryside<br>• a white shirt with embroidery<br>• Arturo's Poems |

        **Content Standard(s): 2**
        **Process Standard(s): 3.5**

2.    Examples of top score-point responses:

- It is important to respect your elders and learn from them. Arturo took his grandfather for granted and usually ignored him. After spending some time with his grandfather, Arturo realized that he was a complex, talented, and wise individual. Arturo began to admire his grandfather after he got to know him a little better.

- It is important to pursue your dreams. Some dreams require hard work and great sacrifice. Arturo wants to pursue his dreams. He feels that his grandfather may not have worked hard enough to achieve his goals. The boy also learns that his grandfather faced tremendous obstacles. The boy will not have to face those same obstacles. The boy is determined to succeed.

   **Content Standard(s): 2**
   **Process Standard(s): 3.5**

3.    Example of top score-point response:

- Arturo is stubborn and ambitious. His grandfather has titled his book *Así es la vida*, which means "That's the way life is." Arturo's philosophy is that life is what you make it. Commenting on his grandfather, the narrator says, "I think he could've been a teacher if he had wanted to bad enough. Nobody is going to stop me from doing what I want with my life. I'm not going to let *la vida* get in my way." Life is not going to keep Arturo down. The boy doesn't fully understand the cultural barriers that his grandfather faced. Still, the boy is determined to succeed in life, no matter what obstacles he faces.

   **Content Standard(s): 2**
   **Process Standard(s): 3.5**

4.    Example of top score-point response:

- After listening to his grandfather for an hour, Arturo has newfound respect and admiration for the old man. Arturo will probably sit with the senior citizens and listen to his grandfather recite poetry. Arturo has told his mother to wait a little while longer. This afternoon probably marks the beginning of a deeper friendship between Arturo and his grandfather.

   **Content Standard(s): 2**
   **Process Standard(s): 3.5**

### *Waiting* (page 601)

1.    Example of top score-point response:

- During the play, Juliette's dress ripped in the back, along the zipper. She found herself stranded onstage because the taffeta had torn. It could have been a horribly embarrassing situation. Thinking quickly, Henrietta "glided onstage." She took a bedspread and pinned it on her sister, carefully using a safety pin. Henrietta acted as though she were a character in the play. The bedspread was like a cape. Henrietta's gesture saved her sister, but it also drew a lot of attention to Henrietta herself.

   **Content Standard(s): 2**
   **Process Standard(s): 3.5**

2. Examples of top score-point responses:

Juliette         Henrietta

| Dominant and bossy | Submissive and quiet |
|---|---|
| 1. Very athletic | Not interested in sports |
| 2. Hair is "a mop of wild black curls" | Straight, beige hair |
| 3. Outgoing, draws a lot of attention to herself | Reserved, sits on the sidelines and does not draw attention to herself |
| Other possibilities:<br>• Flamboyant and very emotional<br>• "Broad snub nose"<br>• Very healthy | Other possibilities:<br>• Serene and often expressionless<br>• "Straight little nose"<br>• Prone to getting colds |

**Content Standard(s): 2**
**Process Standard(s): 1.6**

3. Examples of top score-point responses:

- The comments in parentheses talk about how the play was staged. George Cruikshank played a horse, so he acted like he was eating grass. The kids used a wooden spoon and a pickling kettle to make the sound of drums.

- These parenthetical comments allow the author to describe the ways that the children staged the play. In the first parenthetical comment, the author is describing how the boy George Cruikshank made his portrayal of a horse more realistic by acting like he was eating grass. In the second parenthetical comment, the author describes the way that the children created the theatrical effect of a drum roll by using a spoon and kettle. These parenthetical comments allow the reader to understand the charming and amateur nature of the children's theatrical production.

**Content Standard(s): 2**
**Process Standard(s): 3.5**

4. Examples of top score-point responses:

- The narrator used the name "The Grove" to refer to a grove of trees on a plot of land owned by her father. The narrator tells the reader, "There was a small woodlot to the east of the village, on land owned by my father. We called it The Grove." This area was where the narrator and her sister played, and it was also where the kids put on their theatrical production.

- The Grove was where Juliette and Henrietta played the game where they imagined that Nazi soldiers were attacking. The Grove was near the sea, and it could be a spooky place when there was a lot of fog. One time, Juliette tied Henrietta to a tree in The Grove and accidentally forgot about her for a while. Henrietta then became sick with bronchitis, but she never told on her sister. The Grove was also where they staged their summer plays.

**Content Standard(s): 2**
**Process Standard(s): 3.5**

5. Example of top score-point response:

| PLOT ELEMENT | FUNCTION | EXAMPLE(S) |
|---|---|---|
| Exposition | introduces characters and setting | The main characters are Juliette and Henrietta. The setting is Canada in the early 1940s. |
| Rising Action | is where the main conflict unfolds | Juliette often bosses around and complains about her twin sister, Henrietta. |
| Climax | is the turning point of the story | Henrietta pins a blanket on Juliette during the play, and she also begins to attract the attention of boys. |
| Falling Action | follows the climax, and may provide a resolution to the main conflict | Juliette becomes jealous of her twin and stops bossing her around. Now the tables have turned, and Juliette is in Henrietta's shadow. |

**Content Standard(s): 2**
**Process Standard(s): 3.5**

### from *Growing Up* (page 621)

1. Examples of top score-point responses:

- The author's mother made him do this. She set up a meeting with an executive of the Curtis Publishing Company. The author's mother wanted him to "make something of himself" and not be lazy. She felt that selling magazines would be a good way to get him started on a career.

- The author's mother forced him to take this job. The passage is set in the Depression, and the family was very poor. The family probably needed the boy's income, even though it was small.

**Content Standard(s): 3**
**Process Standard(s): 3.5**

2.  Examples of top score-point responses:

- The conversation with the executive from the Curtis Publishing Company is humorous because the boy's mother does all the talking. All that Russell says is, "That's right." It's a funny scene because the mother keeps answering for her son. Another funny scene describes little seven-year-old Doris aggressively selling magazines to people in cars. The author writes, "The driver, probably startled at what he took to be a midget assaulting his car, lowered the window to stare, and Doris thrust a *Saturday Evening Post* at him." Comparing Doris's sales technique to a midget assaulting a car is humorous.

- One funny scene describes Russell telling an elderly uncle that he would like to be a garbage man when he grows up. This scene is funny because the uncle had asked Russell if he wanted to become the President of the United States. The author also uses exaggeration for comic effect. In one scene, the publishing executive gives Russell a canvas bag for carrying magazines. The author writes, "He presented it with reverence fit for a chasuble." By comparing the bag to a priest's garment, the author is poking fun at the seriousness of the executive.

**Content Standard(s): 3**
**Process Standard(s): 3.5**

3.  Examples of top score-point responses:

- In the young boy's mind, being a writer seemed like an easy job, especially compared with being a magazine sales person. The author writes, "Writers did not have to trudge through the town peddling from canvas bags, defending themselves against angry dogs, being rejected by surly strangers. Writers did not have to ring doorbells. So far as I could make out, what writers did couldn't even be classified as work." The young boy didn't realize how much labor was involved with becoming a writer. Russell Banks did, however, grow up to be a great writer.

- The boy's mother often complained that he didn't have "gumption." By this, she meant that he was lazy and didn't have much initiative. The boy knew that he had to do something that would please his mother. Being a writer seemed like a job that would satisfy her, but it also seemed like a job that did not require a lot of grueling, unpleasant work. In the young boy's mind, being a writer didn't even seem like it could "be classified as work."

**Content Standard(s): 3**
**Process Standard(s): 3.5**

4.  Example(s):

- Student diagrams should include the author with his canvas bag, and at least two stores. The diagrams should also be labeled. Some of the businesses were "two filling stations at the intersection with Union Avenue, as well as an A&P, a fruit stand, a bakery, a barber shop, Zuccarelli's drugstore, and a diner shaped like a railroad car."
  **Content Standard(s): 3, 4**
  **Process Standard(s): 2.1**

### from *Exploring the* Titanic (page 658)

1.  Examples of top score-point responses:

    *   According to the label in the diagram, "The forecastle area held giant anchor chains and bollards for tying the ship when in port."

    *   This part of the ship held equipment for tying the ship up when it was in a port. This front part of the ship consisted of crew living and eating areas, crew working areas, and cargo and stores areas.

    **Content Standard(s): 3, 5**
    **Process Standard(s): 3.5**

2.  Examples of top score-point responses:

    *   According to a footnote, stokers were "workers who tended the boilers that powered steamships."

    *   According to the diagram, stokers "had to shovel coal to power the boilers." This was a difficult, dirty job. The boilers made the ship's engines function.

    **Content Standard(s): 3, 5**
    **Process Standard(s): 3.5**

3.  Examples of top score-point responses:

    *   The author compares the ship to a layer cake in order to illustrate that different people were housed on different levels of the ship. Like the layers of a cake, the ship's inhabitants were divided into different "levels." The people on the ship were divided along class/status lines.

    *   The bottom layer of the ship had manual workers. The next layer had third-class passengers, many of whom were Europeans relocating to the United States. Next were the people in the "middle layer," the second-class passengers (e.g., teachers and merchants). Finally, there were the wealthiest passengers, the aristocratic people.

    **Content Standard(s): 3**
    **Process Standard(s): 1.6**

4.  Example of a top score-point response:

    1.  Titan
    2.  Olympic
    3.  New York

    Other possible responses:

    *   Caronia
    *   Californian
    *   Carpathia

    **Content Standard(s): 3**
    **Process Standard(s): 3.5**

5.  Examples of top score-point responses:

    •   The ship hit an iceberg. The ship was severely damaged in this collision. The ship's lower areas filled with water, causing the *Titanic* to sink.

    •   The captain did not give enough serious thought to the numerous warnings about severe ice in the ship's path. Many people thought that the ship would never sink. Perhaps the captain was overconfident. The ship struck an iceberg, the hull was damaged, and the *Titanic* sunk. The ship's crew sent out distress signals, but no ship came to the rescue until after the *Titanic* had sunk.

    **Content Standard(s): 3**
    **Process Standard(s): 3.5**

### *Last Cover* (page 679)

1.  Example(s):

| Differences Between the Brothers |
| --- |
| 1. Colin was interested in art, but the narrator was more interested in working the land. The narrator was, therefore, more similar to the boys' father. |
| 2. The narrator helped out with the chores more than Colin did. |
| 3. The narrator was strong and healthy, but Colin was small and often sick. |

| Similarities Between the Brothers |
| --- |
| 1. Both boys love the fox, Bandit. |
| 2. Both boys enjoy spending time outdoors in the woods. |
| 3. The boys shared a strong bond during the hunt for the fox. |

    **Content Standard(s): 2, 4**
    **Process Standard(s): 1.6, 1.8**

2.  Examples of top score-point responses:

    •   The father was referring to animals that hibernate or take shelter when winter weather arrives. He also had an old rhyming expression that named these seven animals: bear, bat, woodchuck, raccoon, chipmunk, skunk, and mouse.

    •   According to Granther Yeary's rhyme, the seven sleepers were surly bear, sooty bat, brown chuck, masked coon, chippy-munk, sly skunk, and mice. Yeary also noted that man would have joined the group "if he'd had a little more sense."

    **Content Standard(s): 2**
    **Process Standard(s): 3.5**

3.  Examples of top score-point responses:

    •   Bandit had a "sanctuary" that was a pool of water. He could jump in a stream, swim downstream, and stay hidden in a deep pool. This fooled the hunters and the dogs.

    •   The fox eluded the dogs by jumping in water and swimming. This made it more difficult for the hunting dogs to detect Bandit's scent. The fox had a deep pool that was a hiding place. Bandit also got other foxes to come out and run. Often, the hunting dogs would chase those foxes instead of chasing Bandit.

    **Content Standard(s): 2**
    **Process Standard(s): 3.5**

ANSWER KEY
UNIT 5

4. Examples of top score-point responses:

- The father knew that the fox was a wild animal that could not be fully tamed. He also predicted that the fox would kill the family's chickens. He was right. Bandit was eating chickens, which were supposed to be for the family, not for a fox.

- The father warned the boys about their "soft ways," or gentle treatment of the fox. The father warned, "Remember, you can't make a dog out of a fox." The father knew that the boys would become very attached to Bandit. The fox, however, was a wild animal. The father knew that the fox would one day want to go live on its own.

**Content Standard(s): 2**
**Process Standard(s): 3.5**

5. Examples of top score-point responses:

- This drawing symbolizes Colin's desire to become an artist. He does not want to be a farmer. The father's approval and acceptance of the drawing showed his acknowledgment of his son's artistic skill. The father had previously looked down on Colin's artwork. Now, however, he begins to accept it. This drawing symbolizes a change in the relationship between Colin and his father. Colin now has his father's emotional support.

- This drawing symbolizes Colin's personality. It shows his love of nature, his artistic talent, his affection for Bandit, and his desire for his father's approval. This framed drawing is symbolic of all the things that Colin thinks are important in life.

**Content Standard(s): 2**
**Process Standard(s): 1.6, 3.5**

## *A Crown of Wild Olive* (page 709)

1. Examples of top score-point responses:

- The Double Stade was a footrace twice the length of a stadium. It was the Four Hundred Yards race. The starting line was made of limestone curbs. A trumpet sound announced the start of the race.

- In the Double Stade, the athletes would run toward the turning post, then circle around it and run back toward the winning post. It was like running the length of the stadium twice. Amyntas won the race.

**Content Standard(s): 2**
**Process Standard(s): 3.5**

2. Examples of top score-point responses:

- Amyntas was from Athens, and Leon was from Sparta. Athens and Sparta were at war. During the Games Festival, a truce was called so that the athletes could travel to Olympia and compete in peace. Amyntas and Leon were competing in the same event, so that also made it difficult for them to be friends.

- Amyntas becomes friends with Leon, who, in a way, is really the enemy. He is the enemy because he is a Spartan. He is also the enemy because he was a runner in the Double Stade race. Amyntas and Leon both hoped that they would not meet on the battlefield in the future.

**Content Standard(s): 2**
**Process Standard(s): 1.6**

3.  Examples of top score-point responses:

    • If Leon had not cut his foot, then he would have won the race. His injury caused him to miss some crucial training days. He was leading the race, but then his cut reopened and started bleeding. There's no way that a runner can do his best when his foot is bleeding. That injury cost him the race.

    • Even if Leon had not cut his foot, Amyntas still would have won the race. This race was so important that Leon wouldn't have allowed a minor cut to slow him down significantly. When the runners are discussing the injury, Leon says to Amyntas, "Do you really think that could make any difference? It would take more than a cut foot to slow me up, Athenian!—You ran the better race, that's all." Leon admitted that his cut was not the reason that he lost the race.

    **Content Standard(s): 2**
    **Process Standard(s): 3.5**

4.  Examples of top score-point responses:

    • Leon had no money, and he did not want to buy anything. He came from Sparta, a city-state that did not use money. So, he couldn't have bought anything even if he had wanted to.

    • Spartans didn't use money very much. They had no system of coinage. They used heavy iron bars instead of money. These were not very practical, and you couldn't really carry them around over long distances. Leon was a Spartan, and the Spartans "were very proud of their freedom from wealth."

    **Content Standard(s): 2**
    **Process Standard(s): 3.5**

5.  Example(s):

    | Differences Between the Ancient Games and the Modern Games |
    |---|
    | 1. Today, athletes come from different countries, not different city-states. |
    | 2. Today, athletes wear special running shoes, instead of being barefoot. |
    | 3. Today, the athletes who come in first, second, and third are given gold, silver, and bronze medals. |
    | 4. Today, there would be no water shortage at the Games. |
    | 5. Today, women are allowed to compete in the Games. |

    | Similarities Between the Ancient Games and the Modern Games |
    |---|
    | 1. Athletes still travel great distances to compete in the Games. |
    | 2. Track and field events are still an important part of the summer Olympic Games. |
    | 3. Nearly all the athletes are under age 35, and many of them are teenagers; the Games remain very youth-oriented. |
    | 4. Athletes still work with trainers who help them to improve their performances. |
    | 5. Spectators still gather in the thousands in order to cheer and purchase souvenirs. |

    **Content Standard(s): 2, 4**
    **Process Standard(s): 1.6, 1.8**

### from **Long Walk to Freedom** (page 732)

1.  Examples of top score-point responses:

    • Nelson Mandela writes, "I have walked that long road to freedom." Here, he is comparing the political struggles of his life to a journey down a road. Comparing life to a walk down a road is a common metaphor. Mandela also writes that an oppressor is, himself, "locked behind the bars of prejudice and narrow-mindedness." Here, he is comparing the condition of having a closed mind to the condition of being locked inside a prison.

    • Nelson Mandela writes, "My country is rich in the minerals and gems that lie beneath its soil, but I have always known that its greatest wealth is its people, finer and truer than the purest diamonds." Here, he is comparing the character of a people to the value and beauty of a diamond. Mandela also writes that his family "paid a terrible price" due to his commitment to political causes. He does not mean a monetary price, but rather an emotional sacrifice. In another metaphor, Mandela compares the end of apartheid to the moment when you reach the top of a great hill.

    **Content Standard(s): 3**
    **Process Standard(s): 1.6**

2.  Examples of top score-point responses:

    • Mandela means that even though he is out of prison, and even though apartheid has been abolished, there is still much work to be done. He views the end of apartheid as the continuation of his journey—not the end of his journey.

    • The author means that you can't stop working just because you have achieved some important goals. You have to keep fighting and struggling to improve yourself and those around you. The quest for justice is a never-ending struggle.

    **Content Standard(s): 3**
    **Process Standard(s): 3.5**

3.  Examples of top score-point responses:

    • When Mandela was a boy, he was not aware of the laws of apartheid. He had a joyous childhood. He writes, "As long as I obeyed my father and abided by the customs of my tribe, I was not troubled by the laws of man or God." When he became an adult, Mandela realized that his "boyhood freedom was an illusion." Because of his skin color, he could not stay out at night, read what he pleased, or go where he chose. He was also denied the "basic and honorable freedoms" of achieving his potential.

    • When Mandela was a boy, he was naive because he was merely a child. He did not realize that there were racist laws that oppressed people. When he became an adult, he felt restricted by these racist rules and laws. He no longer felt free. He wanted freedom for himself, for his people, and for his entire nation.

    **Content Standard(s): 3**
    **Process Standard(s): 3.5**

### The Elephant (page 740)

1.   Examples of top score-point responses:

   •   The narrator is an elephant who has been tied up with a rope and chain. The emotion he feels is a yearning to be free. He wants to roam freely.

   •   The elephant is the narrator of the poem. He is a wild beast and he wants to roam free. He is tired of being confined. He does not want to be confined by an ankle-ring and a picket-stake. Perhaps people use him as a work animal or as a means of transportation. His emotions center on his desire to be free.

   **Content Standard(s): 2**
   **Process Standard(s): 3.5**

2.   Example of top score-point response:

   •   The writer admires the elephant because of its strong will and ambition. The elephant is determined to break free of his chains. The author depicts the animal as a noble creature. The repetition of the phrase "I will" shows the fierceness of the elephant's determination.

   **Content Standard(s): 2**
   **Process Standard(s): 3.5**

### The Turtle (page 740)

1.   Example of top score-point response:

   •   The turtle comes out of the pond, climbs a hill, digs a nest in the sand, and lays her eggs. The narrator observes that the turtle is compelled to do this because she is part of Nature.

   **Content Standard(s): 2**
   **Process Standard(s): 3.5**

2.   Example of top score-point response:

   •   The "wish" is the animal's instinct to lay her eggs. The poem is about the way that animals don't carefully consider their actions the way that humans do. Instead, they just follow their instincts. This instinct is what leads to the continuation of the species. The turtle is simply doing "what she was born to do."

   **Content Standard(s): 2**
   **Process Standard(s): 3.5**

3.   Examples of top score-point responses:

   •   Both poems are about how animals belong outside in nature. Both authors admire their subjects. The elephant wants to be free, and the turtle feels connected to all the elements of nature surrounding her. The poems are different in terms of the narrator. "The Elephant" has a first-person narrator, and "The Turtle" has an omniscient narrator.

   •   Both poems have a very positive attitude toward animals. In "The Turtle," the poet uses the title as the first words of line 1. The author of "The Elephant" does not do this. Both poems use personification. The elephant is angry at humans, but the turtle does not seem to be aware of any humans.

   **Content Standard(s): 2**
   **Process Standard(s): 1.6**

### from **Anthony Burns: The Defeat and Triumph of a Fugitive Slave** (page 750)

1.  Example of a top score-point response:

    1. That Anthony Burns had escaped from slavery
    2. That Charles F. Suttle owned the slave Anthony Burns
    3. That the prisoner in the courtroom was, in fact, Anthony Burns

    Other possible response:

    - Judge Loring said, "And these are: that Anthony Burns escaped from slavery from the state of Virginia; that Anthony Burns was by the law of Virginia the slave of Charles F. Suttle; that the prisoner is indeed Anthony Burns."

    **Content Standard(s): 3**
    **Process Standard(s): 3.5**

2.  Example of top score-point response:

    - This trial took place in 1854. At that time, slavery was allowed in the state of Virginia, but not in the state of Massachusetts. Anthony Burns escaped from Virginia so that he could live as a free man in Massachusetts, where he was eventually captured. According to the Fugitive Slave Act, escaped slaves living in the North could be forced to return to their lives of slavery in the South.

    **Content Standard(s): 3**
    **Process Standard(s): 3.5**

3.  Examples of top score-point responses:

    - Burns was very scared. He was intimidated by all the people in court, and he could hardly speak. He felt terribly sad because he was convinced that he would be forced to return to Virginia. He was scared the Charles Suttle would beat him.

    - The author says that Anthony Burns felt numb and moved "like a sleepwalker." It seemed, at times, that he was almost hypnotized. He was also weak from a lack of food. The author also describes Burns as appearing "to be in a trance." Burns thought that his plight would be worse if he put up any defense in the courtroom. He thought that any kind of defense would just make Charles Suttle beat him more. Burns was confused, and he may not have fully understood the laws that applied to his case.

    **Content Standard(s): 3**
    **Process Standard(s): 3.5**

4.  Examples of top score-point responses:

    - This was a secret group of abolitionists who could come together very quickly to take action. The committee's main purpose was "to secure the fugitives and colored inhabitants of Boston and vicinity from any invasion of their rights." This was like a Civil Rights group back in the 1800s.

    - The purpose of the Boston Vigilance Committee was to help black people in situations where their rights were being violated. This included escaped slaves. Coming to the legal aid of Anthony Burns was a typical example of the committee's activities.

    **Content Standard(s): 3**
    **Process Standard(s): 3.5**

5.  Example(s):

    *   LAWS SUPPORTING SLAVERY HAVE NO PLACE IN BOSTON! ANTHONY BURNS OF VIRGINIA, LIKE ALL HUMANS, DESERVES TO BE FREE! DO NOT ALLOW THIS MAN TO RETURN TO A HORRID LIFE OF SLAVERY! ALL JUSTICE-LOVING PEOPLE SHOULD WITNESS THIS MAN'S TRIAL ON SATURDAY, MAY 27, 1854.

        **Content Standard(s): 3, 4**
        **Process Standard(s): 1.5, 2.1**

## *The People Could Fly* (page 767)

1.  Examples of top score-point responses:

    *   This story provides hope for the listener. It is a story about slaves who had a magic power that allowed them to fly away to freedom. It is a folk tale that inspired and comforted people who were living a torturous life of slavery. The message is that one day, life will be better than it is today.

    *   Almost every slave probably wished that she or he could just fly away. This tale reminded the slaves that a horrible life cannot continue forever. Things will either get better because you will escape to the North and be free, or, you will leave this existence and have a much better one in the afterlife. Slaves who escaped to the North could gain their freedom. This tale of flying probably encouraged some slaves to secretly travel to the North on the Underground Railroad.

        **Content Standard(s): 2**
        **Process Standard(s): 3.5**

2.  Examples of top score-point responses:

    *   You had to work outside from sunrise to sunset. If the Overseer didn't think that you were working hard enough, then you got whipped. You were whipped until you bled. There was no medicine around to put on your wounds, so they probably became infected. You had no choice but to do the back-breaking jobs that you were forced to do. You had no rights. If you tried to escape and got caught, you were either severely beaten or killed.

    *   Slaves had no civil rights. They were treated like property, and they were physically tortured. Even babies were whipped. Slaves did strenuous, tedious work out in the fields. The Driver would beat them with a whip.

        **Content Standard(s): 2**
        **Process Standard(s): 3.5**

3.  Example(s):

    *   Student diagrams should include the four characters listed above. The diagrams should also be labeled.

        **Content Standard(s): 2, 4**
        **Process Standard(s): 2.1**

## *Prometheus* (page 800)

1. Examples of top score-point responses:
   - Prometheus was "no great admirer" of Zeus. Prometheus wanted Zeus to give fire to humans. Zeus did not like Prometheus's attitude. Prometheus really tried Zeus's patience and got on his nerves. Prometheus defied Zeus by giving fire to humans. Zeus punished him by chaining him to a mountain, where birds ate his liver.
   - Prometheus did not respect Zeus's authority. Zeus tried to explain over and over why humans should not be allowed to have fire. Prometheus would not listen to Zeus. Zeus told him, "Go now and trouble me no more with your speculations." Prometheus gave humans fire even though Zeus did not want him to do this. Zeus harshly punished Prometheus, but Hercules saved him.

   **Content Standard(s): 2**
   **Process Standard(s): 1.6, 3.5**

2. Examples of top score-point responses:
   - Fire allowed them to cook meat, travel at night, make swords, build ships, and form armored armies. Before fire, they lived like cave men. Afterwards, they had technology and civilizations. Fire was the key to this advancement.
   - Zeus feared that giving humans fire would destroy their humility. He thought that fire would cause man to become "poisoned with pride." Fire allows humans to make weapons and ships. Zeus believes that the introduction of fire into human civilization will eventually cause man to destroy himself.

   **Content Standard(s): 2**
   **Process Standard(s): 3.5**

3. Examples of top score-point responses:
   - Zeus became so angry that he considered destroying humans with a thunderbolt. He then stopped and decided to merely observe while humans destroyed themselves. Zeus was fearful that humans would not know how to responsibly handle fire, and that they would become full of pride, almost thinking of themselves as gods. He feels that his fears have now come true. He is full of rage. He has now decided to sit back and watch humans kill each other.
   - The moral is that with new technology comes great responsibility. Humans have not always used technology carefully and wisely. Zeus feels that humans will become arrogant, and this arrogance will lead to their destruction. This is why he did not want people to have fire in the first place.

   **Content Standard(s): 2**
   **Process Standard(s): 3.5**

4.    Examples of top score-point responses:

- Zeus tells Prometheus that humans have the "capacity for worship." Zeus says that this is the reason that humans were made.

- Zeus explains to Prometheus that man's ability to worship made him different from the beasts. Zeus notes that man has "an aptitude for admiring our power, being puzzled by our riddles and amazed by our caprice. That is why he was made." Zeus is basically saying that animals cannot worship gods in the way that people can.

**Content Standard(s): 2**
**Process Standard(s): 1.6, 3.5**

### *Theseus and the Minotaur* (page 804)

1.    Examples of top score-point responses:

- Theseus suspected that there might be treachery at dinner. Instead of drinking from the poisonous winecup, he pulled out his sword to cut the meat. The king immediately recognized the sword, so it must have been one that he had owned or seen long ago. To the king, this sword was proof of his son's identity.

- When King Aegeus saw the sword, he knew that Theseus was his son. The author writes, "Seeing that sword, the king reached out startled, snatched the winecup from Theseus' hand, and dashed it to the floor." Then he hugged Theseus and called him son. The king had stopped his son from drinking poison.

**Content Standard(s): 2**
**Process Standard(s): 3.5**

2.    Examples of top score-point responses:

- The Athenians had to pay a tribute to Minos. They did this by sacrificing youths to the Minotaur. The youths traveled by a ship with a black sail. This black sail showed that the ship was paying a tribute to King Minos and therefore must be allowed to pass safely. Theseus told the Athenians to also travel with a white sail. His plan was to defeat the Minotaur and then return home with a white sail on the ship; this would be a symbol of their victory. He did defeat the Minotaur. On the frantic voyage home, the sailors forgot to change the sail from black to white. King Aegeus saw the black sail and, in grief, committed suicide because he thought his son was dead. This was a tragic mistake. His son was actually alive.

- Theseus had a plan: His ship would return home victorious, with a white sail. This would indicate their victory over the Minotaur. Unfortunately, because they were in a hurry, the sailors forgot to put up the white sail. When Aegeus saw the black sail, he killed himself because he thought his son was dead. Theseus then became king.

**Content Standard(s): 2**
**Process Standard(s): 3.5**

3.      Example(s):

| Ways Ariadne Helped Theseus |
| --- |
| • She pitied him. |
| • She quietly and secretly went to the dungeon to talk to him. |
| • She wore no shoes so that she would make little noise and therefore, not get caught. |
| • She took him to the Labyrinth and whispered to him a secret clue of how to find the center. |
| • She gave him a sword to help him defeat the Minotaur. |
| • She gave him some thread so that he could find his way back out of the Labyrinth. |

**Content Standard(s): 2, 4**
**Process Standard(s): 1.6, 1.8**

4.      Example of top score-point response:

•      This myth explains the formation of a certain constellation that resembles a crown. Ariadne was left behind on the island of Naxos, but a god made her his bride. To mark this event, he placed her crown in the sky, where it became a formation of stars.

**Content Standard(s): 2**
**Process Standard(s): 3.5**

### *Waters of Gold* (page 812)

1.      Examples of top score-point responses:

Simile (Using *like* or *as*)                    Metaphor

| "His hair was as matted and muddy as a bird's nest." | "He was a ragbag of a man." |
| --- | --- |
| 1. "The beggar stood on one leg, just like a crane." | 1. He was "a trash heap." |
| 2. "It's as real as me." | 2. He was "a walking pig wallow." |

Other possibilities:

•      "The rich old woman stood moving her mouth like a fish out of water."
•      "The illness fell away from the old woman, like an old, discarded cloak."
•      "Heaven is my roof."
•      "The whole world [is] my house."
•      "Out of the way, you vultures."
**Content Standard(s): 2**
**Process Standard(s): 3.5**

2.      Examples of top score-point responses:

•      They were not helping out of kindness, but out of greed. They wanted to be rich, just like Aunt Lily. They all wanted gold.

•      At first, the villagers looked down on the beggar because he was dirty and smelly. But after they saw Aunt Lily's gold, they became greedy. They all wanted to help the beggar because they had seen Aunt Lily's reward. The beggar had given Aunt Lily a bucket filled with gold.

**Content Standard(s): 2**
**Process Standard(s): 3.5**

3.     Examples of top score-point responses:

  •   Here, the rich neighbor's own words have come back to haunt her, even though she didn't really notice. When the beggar came to town the first time, she implied that he was "garbage." She said, "Garbage is garbage." When the beggar returns, the woman is eager to help because she wants the gold reward. He sees through her plan.

  •   The beggar's comment indicates that he is not fooled by the rich neighbor's actions. He knows that she is not being generous, because he knows how she treated him previously. The beggar punishes her by turning her water into ants, lizards, and snakes. His comment shows that he has not forgotten her cruel words and actions.

  **Content Standard(s): 2**
  **Process Standard(s): 3.5**

4.     Examples of top score-point responses:

  •   Aunt Lily states the moral: "Kindness comes with no price." Aunt Lily was rewarded with gold because she treated others nicely, expecting nothing in return. The rich, old neighbor was not rewarded with gold because her intentions were not pure.

  •   By the end of the story, the neighbor has learned to be kind. She is no longer greedy. She learns the true meaning of kindness—which is to help people because you should, not because you expect to get a great reward. Another way to state the moral is this: "The act of helping others is its own reward."

  **Content Standard(s): 2**
  **Process Standard(s): 3.5**

### *Ashputtle* (page 818)

1.     Example of a top score-point response:

  1.   She said that Ashputtle was too dusty and dirty.
  2.   She said that Ashputtle did not have the right dress or shoes.
  3.   She said that Ashputtle did not know how to dance.

  Other possible responses:

  •   She said that people would laugh at Ashputtle.
  •   She said that the family would be ashamed of Ashputtle.

  **Content Standard(s): 2**
  **Process Standard(s): 3.5**

2.     Examples of top score-point responses:

  •   He wanted to get the gold slipper off of Ashputtle's foot so that he could learn her true identity. He knew that the slipper would only fit one person.

  •   The king's son danced with a beautiful woman three nights in a row. He did not know who she was, but he wanted to marry her. At the end of each night, the beautiful Ashputtle would escape before the king's son could see her home. The king's son devised a trick to get her gold slipper. The shoe sticks to the stairs. He knew that the gold slipper would only properly fit one woman—and she would become his bride. Ashputtle's identity is revealed when she puts on the slipper.

  **Content Standard(s): 2**
  **Process Standard(s): 3.5**

3.    Examples of top score-point responses:

   •    Repetition helps the reader to anticipate what will happen next. Repetition is also used to emphasize the theme. Examples of repetition include Ashputtle's singing to the birds to get them to help her pick out lentils, and Ashputtle's song that resulted in her radiant dresses. Both of these elements are repeated, and they help the reader to predict what will occur.

   •    Repetition can be used to build excitement in a story. One thing that was repeated was the way that Ashputtle escaped from the king's son after dancing with him. This repetition added suspense. The birds' songs about the stepsisters' bleeding feet also had some repetition. This added drama to the story.

   **Content Standard(s): 2**
   **Process Standard(s): 3.5**

4.    Example(s):

| Importance of Hazel Tree |
|---|
| • The tree symbolizes Ashputtle's love of her mother. |
| • The tree gives her three radiant dresses that help to disguise her identity. |
| • The radiant dresses, which come from the tree, help her to win the heart of the king's son. |
| • The tree also produced the gold slippers, which are the key to her identity being revealed. |
| • The tree helps establish the moral that the kind will be rewarded and the cruel will be punished. |

   **Content Standard(s): 2, 4**
   **Process Standard(s): 1.8**

### *Narcissus* (page 828)

1.    Examples of top score-point responses:

   •    Hera got angry at Echo because she talked so much. Echo did this to help Zeus hide the fact that he was sneaking down to earth to "wander with the nymphs on the mountains."

   •    Hera felt jealous because Zeus liked to spend time with the mountain nymphs. Echo always talked to Hera, and she "kept her listening for hours on end to her stories and her gossip." Hera then realized that Echo was just doing this so that Hera would not notice that Zeus was quietly sneaking back to Olympus. Hera got mad and punished Echo. After that, Echo could only say what others had said first.

   **Content Standard(s): 2**
   **Process Standard(s): 3.5**

2.    Example of top score-point response:

   •    The beautiful youth Narcissus loved no one except himself. He was not interested in any of the nymphs who admired him. He even fell in love with his own reflection in the water. The self-centered nature of the character Narcissus is closely related to the meaning of the modern word narcissism.

   **Content Standard(s): 2**
   **Process Standard(s): 1.6, 3.5**

3.   Examples of top score-point responses:

- Aphrodite was the goddess of love. She felt that when Narcissus rejected Echo, he was rejecting love itself. The goddess saw Narcissus's rejection of love as a personal insult to her. That is why she punished him.

- Aphrodite observed the behavior of Narcissus. Then she said to herself, "And scorning love, he insults me." Aphrodite did not like the way that Narcissus rejected Echo. She punished him by making him fall in love with his own reflection.

   **Content Standard(s): 2**
   **Process Standard(s): 3.5**

4.   Examples of top score-point responses:

- Both characters suffered because they loved someone whom they could not have. Echo loved Narcissus, who rejected her. She "pined away and died." Narcissus also loved someone whom he couldn't have—the beautiful water nymph in the pool, which was actually his own reflection. Narcissus also pined away and died.

- Both characters had broken hearts because they could not have the one they loved. The author notes that Narcissus spent "day after day looking at the only face in the world which he loved—and could not win; and pining just as Echo had pined." Echo and Narcissus both pined away for a loved one.

   **Content Standard(s): 2**
   **Process Standard(s): 1.6, 3.5**

## *Young Arthur* (page 828)

1.   Examples of top score-point responses:

- Arthur was safer there, away from the king's enemies. There was danger near the king, who wanted to protect his son and the true heir to the throne.

- Merlin advised King Uther, "Give the babe into my keeping, for you have enemies even at court." Merlin knew that the rebels would soon try to kill the king and his family. Merlin had Arthur hidden away at Sir Ector's house so that he would not be killed by rebels.

   **Content Standard(s): 2**
   **Process Standard(s): 3.5**

2.  Example(s):

| Differences Between Arthur and Kay |
|---|
| 1. Kay was four years older than Arthur. |
| 2. Kay was a jealous man, but Arthur had a "gentle manner." |
| 3. Arthur was able to withstand wounds without much complaining, but Kay "bellowed loudly" at even the slightest cut. |
| 4. Kay was power-hungry and dishonest, but Arthur was noble. |

| Similarities Between Arthur and Kay |
|---|
| 1. Both lived in Sir Ector's house. |
| 2. Both "knew it was vital to learn the arts of war." |
| 3. Neither one of them knew the identity of King Uther's true heir. |

**Content Standard(s): 2, 4**
**Process Standard(s): 1.6, 1.8**

3.  Examples of top score-point responses:

    • Arthur was so excited about the tournament that he had forgotten to pack Kay's sword. Kay demanded that Arthur go back and get his sword. Along the way, Arthur spotted the sword in the stone and pulled it out. He thought he would borrow it and return it later.

    • Kay made Arthur go back and get his sword. During this journey, Arthur happened to find, and pull out, the sword in the stone. He did not realize the significance of what he had just done. He thought that he would simply put the sword back later. Arthur was able to pull the sword from the stone because he was the king's son and thus, the true heir to the throne.

    **Content Standard(s): 2**
    **Process Standard(s): 3.5**

4.  Examples of top score-point responses:

    • Arthur didn't hear everything that people were saying. He ran away so fast that he didn't understand the significance of pulling the sword from the stone. He mistakenly thought that he had stolen the king's sword.

    • Arthur heard people say, "The king's sword!" The author writes, "Hearing only this much, Arthur thought that he had stolen a king's weapon." Arthur saw people gathering around Kay with the sword, so he fled. Arthur did not fully understand what was happening. He fled too quickly. He panicked. He had not noticed the sword's inscription: "Whoso pulleth out the sword from this stone is born the rightful King of England." He thought that he had done something wrong when he pulled the sword out; however, it was his destiny to pull the sword from the stone.

    **Content Standard(s): 2**
    **Process Standard(s): 3.5**

### *Lazy Peter and His Three-Cornered Hat* (page 832)

1. Examples of top score-point responses:

   - Lazy Peter tells the farmer that he has a magic hat. He also "demonstrates" the power of this magic hat. By talking to the rich farmer and showing him how he could collect money, Lazy Peter earned the farmer's confidence. Lazy Peter also made his scheme more convincing by acting like he was very hesitant to sell the hat.

   - Lazy Peter returned to pick up the money that he had left with the other men. When the farmer saw this, he thought that Lazy Peter was benefiting from his magic hat. In reality, Lazy Peter was fooling him into thinking that magic was at work. The farmer trusted Peter, so he believed in the "magic power" of the hat.

   **Content Standard(s): 2**
   **Process Standard(s): 1.6, 3.5**

2. Examples of top score-point responses:

   | Story Character | The Way Peter Wore His Hat for Him |
   |---|---|
   | 1. Stand Owner | 1. With one corner turned down |
   | 2. Druggist | 2. With one corner turned up |
   | 3. Priest | 3. With one corner twisted to the side |

   **Content Standard(s): 2**
   **Process Standard(s): 3.5**

3. Examples of top score-point responses:

   - This was the final stop in Lazy Peter's elaborate scheme. Most people believe that a priest is honest. Therefore, the farmer did not think that he was being tricked because he witnessed the involvement of a priest. Lazy Peter knew that getting money while standing inside a church would be the most convincing act of them all. Lazy Peter was dishonest, but very clever.

   - The trip to the church erased any doubt in the farmer's mind. Going to the church was Lazy Peter's "trump card." He knew that this would be very convincing to the farmer. The author writes, "The farmer was delighted with this, his doubts were stilled, and he fairly beamed thinking of all the money he was going to make once that hat was his." Visiting the priest was the last step in fooling the farmer. No one would believe that a priest would be involved in a dishonest scheme.

   **Content Standard(s): 2**
   **Process Standard(s): 3.5**

4. Examples of top score-point responses:

- Lazy Peter "needed money, but it was not his custom to work for it." He wanted to get lots of money without doing a lot of work. The trick he played on the rich farmer shows that he would rather steal than work. He wants "the easy way out." The farmer is the same way. He is also greedy. Lazy Peter tells the rich farmer that he does not have to work for a living because the hat works for him. The farmer wants to make a great deal of money without doing any more work.

- The farmer is similar to Lazy Peter because he is attracted to a "get-rich-quick" scheme. Peter wants to get rich quickly by fooling a farmer. The farmer wants to get rich quickly by purchasing a magic hat that will generate money for him. The farmer gives Peter ten thousand pesos in gold and his fine horse, all for the opportunity to own a magic hat. He, like Lazy Peter, is dreaming of a life of laziness.

**Content Standard(s): 2**
**Process Standard(s): 1.6, 3.5**

## *Phaëthon* (page 842)

1. Example of top score-point response:

- Phaëthon's peer, Epaphus, was teasing him about "his parentage." Phaëthon said to his mother, "Give me proof of my noble birth." She sent her son to visit Apollo, his father. Phaëthon asked for evidence that he was, in fact, his son.

**Content Standard(s): 2**
**Process Standard(s): 3.5**

2. Example of a top score-point response:

1. Taurus (the Bull)
2. Sagittarius (the Thracian Archer)
3. Leo (the Lion)
4. Scorpio (the Scorpion)

Other possible responses:

- Cancer (the Crab)
- Northern Plough, or Big Dipper
- The Serpent, or Draco

**Content Standard(s): 2**
**Process Standard(s): 3.5**

3. Examples of top score-point responses:

- Phaëthon asked Apollo to let him drive the sun chariot. Apollo knew that Phaëthon could not handle the chariot, but "the proud youth" refused to listen. He lost control of the chariot, driving too close to earth. Zeus "had to interfere, or the whole world would have perished in flame." To keep the world from being destroyed, Zeus "let fly a powerful thunderbolt against the young charioteer, which dashed the luckless Phaëthon to earth." Nymphs then buried his body.

- Phaëthon died because he was too arrogant. He foolishly thought that he could control the sun chariot. When Zeus saw that the sun chariot might destroy the earth, he hurled a thunderbolt that killed Phaëthon.

**Content Standard(s): 2**
**Process Standard(s): 3.5**

4. Examples of top score-point responses:

- Apollo, being a god, could not break his word. He promised to grant any wish that Phaëthon requested. Even though he knew it would mean the death of his son, Apollo had to keep his word.

- Apollo had taken an oath to always keep his word. He did keep his word, even though it meant the death of Phaëthon. He made a promise, and he had to keep it, so he could not stop Phaëthon from driving the sun chariot. The author writes, "A mortal may, perhaps, break his word, but not so a god who had sworn by the waters of the Styx."

**Content Standard(s): 2**
**Process Standard(s): 3.5**

### The Force of Luck (page 845)

1. Examples of top score-point responses:

- The miller spent $10 of the money on supplies and a good piece of meat. He was then attacked by a hawk that smelled the meat. The hawk flew away with the rest of the money.

- After buying some meat, the miller was attacked by a hawk. In the struggle, the hawk flew off with the bag of money, which now contained $190. Later, one of the men was curious about seeing a hawk's nest in a tree. When a servant removed the nest, the miller found that his bag of $190 was in the hawk's nest.

**Content Standard(s): 2**
**Process Standard(s): 3.5**

2. Examples of top score-point responses:

- Because of this lead, combined with good luck, the man was given a fish that contained a diamond. The money he got from selling the diamond allowed him to start his own business.

- The lead became very valuable when it was put to good use. The fisherman needed lead to weigh down his nets. In exchange for the lead, the fisherman gave the miller the first fish he caught. This fish had a valuable diamond in its stomach.

**Content Standard(s): 2**
**Process Standard(s): 3.5**

3. Examples of top score-point responses:

- The jeweler and his wife wanted to take advantage of the miller and his wife. This was not ethical. They wanted to pay very little money, even though they knew that the diamond was very valuable. The jeweler's wife panicked during her bargaining session, and "blurted out" an offer of fifty thousand dollars. Later, they increased their bid to one hundred thousand dollars.

- They are dishonest. At first, they tried to buy the diamond for a ridiculously small amount of money. While discussing their dishonest plan, the wife chuckled. They thought that they could fool the miller and his wife, but they were wrong. The miller figured out that this was not merely a piece of worthless glass.

**Content Standard(s): 2**
**Process Standard(s): 3.5**

4. Examples of top score-point responses:

- The story supports the idea that money is more important than luck. Money allowed the miller to start his own business. That is how he moved from poverty to prosperity. It was not luck, but money, that allowed him to start his own mill.

- Luck is more important than money. The miller really got everything from luck. The reappearance of both bags of money just shows what a lucky person that the miller was. The miller got a fish that had a diamond in its stomach. That was pure luck, and that was how he was able to prosper.

**Content Standard(s): 2**
**Process Standard(s): 3.5**

### Brother Coyote and Brother Cricket (page 853)

1. Examples of top score-point responses:

Members of Brother Coyote's Army  Members of Brother Cricket's Army

| Fox | Horseflies |
|---|---|
| 1. Lobo | 1. Mosquitoes |
| 2. Badger | 2. Honey bees |
| 3. Tiger | 3. Bumblebees |
| 4. Panther | 4. Yellow jackets |
| 5. Wildcat | 5. Black hornets |
| Other possibilities:<br>• Coon (raccoon)<br>• Possum (opossum)<br>• "Other people with claws and teeth" | Other possibilities:<br>• Red ants<br>• "All the people that have stingers and can stick" |

**Content Standard(s): 2**
**Process Standard(s): 3.5**

2. Example of top score-point response:

- The coyote means that in nature, animals eat one another. This is simply "the way of the world" or "the law of the jungle." The coyote is saying that it is natural for him to prey on other creatures when the opportunity arises. The cricket thinks that this is unfair, so he challenges the coyote to a duel.

**Content Standard(s): 2**
**Process Standard(s): 3.5**

3. Examples of top score-point responses:

- The cricket sings Spanish lyrics. The coyote and the cricket argue when they meet. The fox yells "Retreat!" when he is attacked by insects. These are three examples in which animals are acting like human beings.

- The coyote organizes an army of animals with teeth. The cricket organizes an army of insects. The coyote and the cricket both command their troops to carry out certain orders. The animals in this story act like human beings.

**Content Standard(s): 2**
**Process Standard(s): 3.5**

4. Examples of top score-point responses:

- The final paragraph provides the moral: "Thus a person should avoid being vainglorious and considering himself shrewder than he is. He may be outwitted by his own vanity." In this story, the coyote was defeated by the much smaller cricket because he was too arrogant.

- Arrogance can lead to defeat. The coyote was cocky, and his army was defeated by a bunch of tiny insects. He did not take his opponents very seriously. Sometimes a person's arrogance or overconfidence can lead to trouble. Vanity is often the downfall of a great leader.

**Content Standard(s): 2**
**Process Standard(s): 3.5**

## *How Odin Lost His Eye* (page 858)

1. Examples of top score-point responses:

- Odin felt that he must know more about his enemies. He feared that the frost giants would harm the people of earth, so he traveled down to learn more about the frost giants. During his journey, he "came to one of the roots of the great evergreen tree." There, he found the magic well.

- Odin wanted to help people. He "knew that the frost giants were only waiting for a chance to bring trouble to his children." Odin wanted to protect his children, so he traveled down to earth to gain "more wisdom" and to do more than merely see his enemies.

**Content Standard(s): 2**
**Process Standard(s): 3.5**

2. Examples of top score-point responses:

- Mimir warned Odin that some people regretted drinking from the well. This was because the viewer sees "sorrow and death as well as joy." In other words, looking into the past and the future would mean that you would see horrible things, along with good things.

- Mimir did not want Odin to be upset by seeing images of death and sorrow. Also, he wanted Odin to understand that he would have to pay a precious price in order to drink from the well.

**Content Standard(s): 2**
**Process Standard(s): 3.5**

3. Example of top score-point response:

- Mimir asks Odin for a great sacrifice. Odin considers sacrificing his son, Balder, but he pauses because "indeed that would be a great price!" Mimir reads Odin's mind and then asks not for his son, but for one of his eyes. It seems that Odin is relieved to not have to sacrifice his son.

**Content Standard(s): 2**
**Process Standard(s): 3.5**

4. Examples of top score-point responses:

- Knowledge comes with a price. You cannot gain knowledge without experience, and sometimes experience can cause great pain. Odin wanted to gain more wisdom, and he did, but in the process, he had to sacrifice one of his eyes.

- You must work hard and pay a great sacrifice in order to gain some things in life. Things that cause suffering can sometimes lead to a deeper understanding. One short expression with a similar message is "No pain, no gain." Odin learned a great deal about the future and the past, but he was required to pay a great price.

**Content Standard(s): 2**
**Process Standard(s): 3.5**

### Pumpkin Seed and the Snake (page 861)

1. Examples of top score-point responses:

- The widow kept saying, "If someone could remove this rock from the middle of my garden I would let him marry one of my daughters." Then when the rock would disappear, the widow would laugh and say, "I was only joking." Then the rock would return. This happened a few times before the snake appeared. The snake had been moving the rock back and forth.

- The widow kept making a promise, saying that whoever moved the rock could marry one of her daughters. Then, when the rock was removed, the widow would say that she hadn't really meant it. Then the rock would reappear. She didn't know who was doing this.

**Content Standard(s): 2**
**Process Standard(s): 3.5**

2. Examples of top score-point responses:

- Pumpkin Seed trusted that her mother would be able to kill the snake if it came inside. Apparently, Pumpkin Vine did not have as much confidence in their mother, so she refused to open the door.

- Neither sister wanted to marry a snake! Pumpkin Vine didn't want to even risk letting the snake come inside the house. Pumpkin Seed, however, agrees to open the door. The widow said, "I will kill the snake when he falls asleep." Pumpkin Seed thinks that this plan will work, so she opens the door.

**Content Standard(s): 2**
**Process Standard(s): 1.6, 3.5**

3. Example(s):

- Student diagrams should include Pumpkin Seed and the stream. The diagrams should also be labeled. The bubbles are yellow, white, and/or green. The yellow bubbles turned into gold jewels, the white bubbles turned into silver jewels, and the green bubbles turned into snakes.

**Content Standard(s): 2, 4**
**Process Standard(s): 2.1**

4.   Example of top score-point response:

* The man has some snakeskin in his armpit. Apparently, he transformed himself from an ugly snake into a handsome man. During the transformation, a small patch of snakeskin remained under his arm. This small patch was evidence that the man was also the snake that Pumpkin Seed had been forced to marry.

     **Content Standard(s): 2**
     **Process Standard(s): 3.5**

### *Kelfala's Secret Something* (page 866)

1.   Examples of top score-point responses:

| Simile (Using *like* or *as*) | Metaphor |
|---|---|
| **"Kelfala howled like a ruffled owl."** | **"He rolled himself into a ball."** |
| 1. "Kelfala just looked, his head bowed like a weeping willow." | 1. "You could see and hear all the animals in the forest in this one Kelfala." |
| 2. "Her skin was as smooth as a mirror." | 2. "Wambuna's lips were sealed." |

Other possibilities:
* "The rings sat on her neck like rows of diamonds on a crown."
* Wambuna's "stream of suitors grew smaller, like the village stream itself."
* Kelfala told Wambuna that she was as "proud as the cotton tree."
* Kelfala was "like a cock ready to peck at the yams."
* Wambuna walked "with her head raised up like a large pink rose in early spring."
* "Kelfala, that clown Kelfala!"
* "Now, the bush came alive." (Personification that is closely related to a metaphor)
* The laughter "dragged the two young men with it." (Personification, related to metaphor)
  **Content Standard(s): 2**
  **Process Standard(s): 3.5**

2.   Examples of top score-point responses:

* Wambuna was beautiful and had many suitors. Tradition held that she had to marry the first young man that she spoke to. Each young man tried to do anything that he could to get Wambuna to speak so that she would then have to marry him. That is why they tried to trick her while she was in her garden.

* Each young man wanted her to notice him, speak to him, and then be bound to marry him. They visited her in her garden "always when the elders were having their rest from the hot midday sun." The young men didn't want the elders to interfere with their coaxing and teasing of Wambuna.

     **Content Standard(s): 2**
     **Process Standard(s): 3.5**

3.  Examples of top score-point responses:

- Kelfala's friends (Shortie Bumpie and Longie Tallie) reasoned that Wambuna should marry all three of them or none of them. Longie Tallie says, "She talked to all three of us!" Tradition held that Wambuna must marry the first man that she speaks to. Kelfala's friends argue that since she spoke to the trio all at once, then she would have to marry all three of them—or none of them.

- It seems that Shortie Bumpie and Longie Tallie are really jealous of Kelfala because he has outsmarted everyone and won the hand of the beautiful Wambuna. Because they are jealous, they devise an argument, or a reason, as to why Kelfala cannot claim Wambuna as his bride. They come up with the unrealistic solution that Wambuna should marry all three of them. They also suggest that she should marry none of them.

**Content Standard(s): 2**
**Process Standard(s): 3.5**

4.  Examples of top score-point responses:

- At the end of the story, Kelfala grinned and said, "There is still tomorrow. There will always be another secret." That means that Kelfala will keep trying to win the hand of Wambuna. He is optimistic and determined to have her as his bride. He will keep on playing tricks on her.

- Kelfala will continue to play tricks on Wambuna. He will do this until she speaks to him and then marries him. Kelfala is too funny and too clever to fail. He will probably tell his friends, "Okay, you are right. Wambuna should not marry any of us." Then, Kelfala will wait until he and Wambuna are alone again, and he will trick her into speaking. Then she will marry him.

**Content Standard(s): 2**
**Process Standard(s): 3.5**

# Scoring Guide for Writing Prompts

## 4 Points

The paper:

- Has an effective beginning, middle, and end.
- Uses paragraphing appropriately.
- Contains a strong controlling idea.
- Progresses in a logical order.
- Uses effective cohesive devices (such as transitions, repetition, pronouns, parallel structure).
- Clearly addresses the topic and provides specific and relevant details/examples.
- Uses precise and vivid language.
- Contains sentences that are clear and varied in structure.
- Effectively uses writing techniques (such as imagery, humor, point of view, voice).
- Clearly shows an awareness of audience and purpose.
- Contains few errors in grammar usage, punctuation, capitalization and/or spelling.

## 3 Points

The paper:

- Has a beginning, middle, and end.
- Uses paragraphing.
- Contains a controlling idea.
- Generally progresses in a logical order.
- May use cohesive devices.
- Addresses the topic and uses relevant details/examples.
- Uses language that is usually precise.
- Contains sentences that are clear and show some variety in structure.
- Uses writing techniques.
- Shows an awareness of audience and purpose.
- May contain errors in grammar usage, punctuation, capitalization, and/or spelling that are not distracting to the reader.

### 2 Points

The paper:

- Has evidence of a beginning, middle, and end.
- Shows evidence of paragraphing.
- Contains some sense of direction, but may lack focus.
- May not progress in a logical order.
- At times seems awkward and lacks cohesion.
- Addresses the topic, but may contain some details that are not relevant.
- May use imprecise language.
- Contains sentences that are generally clear, but lack variety in structure.
- May use writing techniques.
- Shows some awareness of audience and purpose.
- Contains errors in grammar usage, punctuation, capitalization, and/or spelling that may be distracting to the reader.

### 1 Point

The paper:

- May lack evidence of a beginning, middle, and/or end.
- May lack evidence of paragraphing.
- Is difficult to follow and lacks focus.
- Does not progress in a logical order, and may digress to unrelated topics.
- Is awkward and lacks cohesion.
- May address the topic, but lacks details.
- Uses imprecise language.
- Contains sentences that are unclear and lack variety in structure.
- Does not use writing techniques.
- Shows little or no awareness of audience or purpose.
- Contains repeated errors in grammar usage, punctuation, capitalization, and/or spelling that are distracting to the reader.